Am I Normal If?

Susan Kaye, PhD

To your
you with you!
Celebrate

Susan
Kaye

Praise for Dr Susan Kaye

Susan Kaye is a well-respected somatic arts pioneer who normalizes what she calls "Plain Damn You", giving the reader comfort and permission to be who you are! – Dr Patti Britton

Dr. Susan's perspectives on sexuality and gender identity affirmed my own beliefs and experiences in many respects, but they also got me looking at some issues in a new light. - Stephanie Ward, Editor at www.eatsshootsedits.com

Dr. Susan Kaye is a courageous pioneer and revLOVEutionary in the field of surrogacy. It's because of her tireless lifework that this sacred art is accessible to those who so desperately need it. Share this book with all! - ~Bella LaVey, Certified Human Potential Coach and Author: *Fetish Girl*

Dr. Susan Kaye masterfully illustrates the importance of human touch and the many roles it plays in our lives… Her own unique insights, experiences and background create tools and pathways that help you find "Plain Damn You". ~ Paul Tantraviking Bagge, Sex & Intimacy Coach, SPT, Sexological Bodyworker

I find the book to be as equally enlightening, engaging, progressive and informing as my many years of experience working with Dr Susan Kaye. She's told me many times over the years … to do this work … "You need to possess that quality I can't teach you." - Rachel Laird, Tantra Teacher

Sex Therapy evolved from the research of Masters and Johnson in the 1960s. M and J would be proud of the work of Dr. Susan Kaye. She has taken their integrative therapy, that of both the mind and the body to the next level. Readers of Am I Normal if? will have a new understanding of its value to sex therapy clients. - Mark Schoen, Ph.D. Founder, SexSmartFilms.com

Praise for Dr Susan Kaye

Dr. Susan Kaye's "Am I Normal If" is a brilliant, yet gentle book explaining one of the greatest crimes in history - The Miseducation of youth and especially women about sex and their bodies. ... a global conspiracy ... has existed since the beginning of time in most cultures, most major religions, belief systems, educational systems, and cultures, the book is neither angry nor accusatory. It simply explains the tragic consequence of the lack of true sex education, prejudicial science, male superiority and female inferiority myths, political and religious beliefs that are still leading to mental illness, sexual dysfunction, domestic violence, divorce, and in many cases the exploitation, mutilation, enslavement, and trafficking of men and especially women. - KOOGE, Self-Empowerment Educator

"This unpretentious and accessible book is for those who have lots of questions about sexual normality. Dr. Kaye is a passionate hands-on practitioner who believes in the importance of touch and listening to the body for those answers. Identifying the nature/nurture influences that shape our sexuality, she ultimately wants the reader to appreciate their unique diversity and be comfortable with being "Plain. Damn.You." - Rev. Dr. Beverly Dale, Founder of the Incarnation Institute for Sex & Faith

"Am I Normal If" is based on the tremendous work and expertise of Dr. Susan Kaye. As a women's lifestyle doctor, I recommend this book as the best resource for my clients on the topic of sexuality. Many tough questions have been answered and explained effortlessly through clients' stories, case studies, and scientific facts. This book is very educational as well as entertaining and easy to read. I would highly encourage you to follow the work of Dr. Kaye, a very experienced and knowledgeable practitioner, who is changing the lives of thousands of people. - Larisa Sharipova is trained as a Medical Doctor and practices as a Certified Holistic Health Practitioner. She is a founder of Holistic Expert, LLC

Praise for Am I Normal If?

This book is a big contribution to the field of human sexuality. "Am I normal if" is book therapy like none other. It is a huge contribution to the field of human sexuality. It is an updated understanding of our evolving humanity and everything related to it. Friendly, informative, and an emotional reading for everyone who lives in a body. - Carolina Laínez, Surrogate Partner Therapist

Dr. Kaye has written a fascinating, informative book about being "normal." If any such thing exists! By posing numerous questions she helped me look at my own life and examine the love, abuse, and denial that created "me", my sexual partners and career choices. - Gina Gilbert, Artist, Acupuncturist, Movement Therapist

Dr. Kaye's book is a fascinating, informative must-read for Every Body, Mind, and Spirit. The questions, stories, and links, were tremendously helpful in understanding my own early experiences and messages about love and sex. Bravo Dr Susan! – GG, Bodyworker

Dr. Kaye is a riveting writer and her messages transcend norms, leading the way to integrative approaches to sexual medicine, therapy, and coaching. I highly recommend this book! - *Dr. Patti Britton, Sexologist, "Mother of Sex Coaching" and Co-Founder of SexCoachU.com (and DrPattiBritton.com)*

"In 'Am I Normal If' renowned sex therapist and founder of Integrated Mind-Body Therapy, Dr. Susan Kaye walks us through the process she uses to help clients discover who they truly are in the bedroom, liberating them from self-imposed limitations around their sexuality. This deep-dive journey is well worth taking!" - Epiphany Jordan, author of *Somebody Hold Me: The Single Person's Guide to Nurturing Human Touch*

Praise for Am I Normal If?

A priceless resource for Therapy and Counseling professionals, Sexuality professionals, students, or anyone seeking to understand themselves on a deeper level. ~ Paul Tantraviking Bagge, Sex & Intimacy Coach, SPT, Sexological Bodyworker

Dr. Susan Kaye's Am I Normal IF? provides solid information about human sexual growth, from childhood--You with You, to sharing intimacy--You with Others, into maturity-- Plain Damn You. This book is a "body owner's manual," inviting us to live our own fingerprint—to listen to, cherish and share our unique being. No wonder her clients still send her cards 30 years later. - Rachel Laird, Tantra Teacher

One of the greatest things about this book is Dr. Susan's conversational style, which will attract readers who wouldn't normally read the works of a scholarly writer. I feel like I'm in a room talking to her, and her compassion and enthusiasm for her work shine through. - Stephanie Ward, Editor at www.eatsshootsedits.com

'Am I Normal?' is an Informative, loving, and gentle read with Dr. Susan Kaye's authentic voice clearly heard throughout the pages as she reaches out to encourage, inspire and assist people to discover the happiness and fulfilment of their sexual self, enriching every facet of their life potential. - Beverley Anne Foster – Relationship and sexuality consultant, writer, producer, director and acting coach.

"Who hasn't asked themselves the question Dr. Susan Kaye answers in her new book, Am I Normal If? That one question touches each of us in different ways. Dr. Kaye addresses the question from cradle to grave, taking the reader through her own life, and encouraging the reader to examine their own." - Ricci Joy Levy, President and CEO of The Woodhull Freedom Foundation

Title: Am I Normal If?

First Published in July 2022

Published in Texas, United States

The author and publisher specifically disclaim any liability, loss or risk which is incurred as a consequence, directly or indirectly, of the use and application of any content of this work.

ISBN 13 - 978-0-578-28221-3

Cover Design by Susan Kaye & Nikki Leigh

Book Design & Layout by Nikki Leigh

Editing by Nikki Leigh

Copyright © 2022 Dr Susan Kaye

Published by Integrative Mind-Body Therapies, LLC

Dedication

Dedicated to Mother Nature who knows only diversity. Every snowflake, tree, plant, flower, and creature is unique. Here is where normal celebrates the differences that make our planet beautiful and enriches our existence. As it is with the contribution of each and every human whose gift is Divine Diversity.

To my three daughters who have a very not "normal" mom, the three of you are incredible and accomplished women.

To my partner, Jerry, whose support included making a lot of spaghetti dinners and "nagging" with daily questions including, "Working on the book today?" "Is the book done?" "Need me to do anything while you work on the book?" All of which gave me encouragement and determination to get 'er done.

Table of Contents

Foreword

Thirty-five years ago, I received a call from a young woman, Susan Kaye, asking me if she could meet with me to talk about the field of human sexuality. She was in a master's degree program at Villanova University. When she came to my office, I found her to be very inquisitive about the field, telling me she was trained as a massage therapist and was using this work to pay for Villanova. When she touched certain areas of their bodies, clients would often become emotional and tell her certain memories were coming up. At times, very intimate stories would come out. She didn't know what to do or say.

I invited Susan to visit a graduate class I was teaching at the University of Pennsylvania on the topic of sex therapy. She was convinced her clients had very little knowledge about human sexuality. She asked if we had any massage therapists in our clinical practice office. I told her we had never even thought about adding a massage therapist to our practice. She believed that she could be very helpful to our clients and therapists. We set up one of our group rooms with a table, soft music, and low lights. Several of our therapists started referring their clients to Susan and were soon getting stories from these clients that only came out through their massage experiences, and they benefited from her working with their therapists.

One time I had a sexual surrogate, Anne, from New York City come to speak to my students at the University of Pennsylvania, and I invited Susan to that class. It was a "WOW" moment for Susan, and she decided to spend some time with Anne to learn about surrogacy and how it could be helpful to some of our clients who had no access to sexual partners.

At the same, time she was invited to work with clients from the Masters and Johnson therapy clinic program in St. Louis. Over the next several years, through using a hands-on approach, I saw actual miracles take place. We developed a Masters-and-Johnson-model triadic relationship with the client, verbal therapist, and body therapist. This became our model.

After Susan graduated from Villanova and because of so many positive client experiences, I talked Susan into going on for her doctorate in human sexuality at the Institute for the Advanced Study of Human Sexuality in San Francisco. Her doctoral dissertation was on *Surrogate Treatment: A Case Study of 151 Male Clients and Surrogacy.* All of the above added up to many years of experience teaching, training, and practicing as a sexologist.

Susan has gathered information from and asked questions of hundreds of clients, students, and therapists. Now she has the opportunity to impart this information to us in this imaginative book on questions to explore with clients. This book–based on the foundational question "Am I normal if?"– is relevant to students, practitioners, and the general public.

What is most exciting to me is the process she uses in explaining how she learns so much from exploring the messages that the body is giving through the memories and stories that are evoked through touch. As a psychotherapist, I would learn things from Susan that verbal therapy might have never brought to the surface, or she brought it out more effectively. She offers many stories that come up, about a person's relationship with themselves (You with You), from early in life, from religion, and to hopefully developing self-pleasure. This is all within the You with You section of the book, laying a foundation for the next section of the book.

Next Dr. Kaye explores the stories that are evoked in relationships with others (You with Others). She covers first relationship encounters, which may be positive or negative, that are part of the socialization process that everyone goes through. There are helpful personal stories that shed light on the fears one may have about relationships. The issues of self-confidence, personal experiences, both positive and negative, the role of shyness and anxiety, all of which can block a person's ability to develop close and intimate relationships, are detailed in the book.

All these topics illuminate the place of nature and/or nurture in a person's life, shaping each person's own "Plain Damn You." In the end, Susan discusses each individual's personal "normal"—what is natural and normal for them. Because of the multitude of differences in clients, she makes the case for a belief in diversity and the need for reverence and respect for all people. She concludes with the concept of LOVE being important to a healthy "normal."

What was so beneficial to me was asking myself all the questions that she asked her clients. Reading her book opened up for me things in my own story that I had not explored before. It was a personal growth experience for me that should also excite you, about you.

William R. Stayton, MDiv., ThD., PhD.

Retired Professor and Director

Program in Human Sexuality Studies

Widener University, Chester, PA

Retired Professor and Assistant Director

Center of Excellence for Sexual Health

Satcher Health Leadership Institute

Morehouse School of Medicine, Atlanta, GA

AASECT - Retired Certified Educator, Therapist, Supervisor, and Diplomate

Author, *Sinless Sex: A Challenge to Religions.* (2020)

Luminare Press.

Preface

Have you ever questioned even for one moment, do I fit in, are my legs too short, or is my nose too long? Why can't I look like, act like, or feel like so and so...?

If you can identify with these questions, this book is for you! The "am I normal if, scared, lost, frustrated hopeless" you. The you that needs or wants a guide, to know and embrace your own unique fingerprint, snowflake, and to discover your gift to the planet.

The motivation for what is "normal" came early in my career as a Human Sexuality Professor. It was early 2000 in the small town where I grew up. It was with inspired students who were just out of high school and testing the education waters in a Community College. The question of why people are gay was a hot topic back then. There was a flurry of discussions about the "cause" of being gay:

1. they are made that way,

2. they had an absentee father or mother,

3. they just want attention,

4. is it nature or is it nurture?

I have a clear memory of walking to the blackboard (yes, we had chalk and blackboards!) and I drew my version of the peace sign:

On the left third I wrote "Nature", on the right I wrote "Nurture" and on the bottom "Plain Damn You"

Take this journey with me so that you can pass it on, like a candle, to enlighten those who struggle with… Am I Normal If….?

During the strategizing and brainstorming for this book, the idea was formed to write the book with my introductory session with new clients in mind. What would I ask and what information would I need to find out about a new client? You will find many questions that will stir memories about the earliest years of your life. That's a good thing. Those are the things that shaped you and influence the decisions you make.

You may want to take notes as you read the book and write things down that come to mind. I think you will be interested to see what you learn about yourself while you're reading the book. Let's get started on the journey to discovery... to find Plain Damn You!

PART ONE –
MEET DR
SUSAN KAYE

Thirds Theory

of

Self-Actualization

Chapter One Meet Dr. Susan Kaye

"The aim of life is to live, and to live means to be aware, joyously, drunkenly, serenely, divinely connected and aware." Henry Miller

When people learn about the kind of work I do, they frequently ask how I came to choose the path to becoming a PhD sexologist. What was the driving force behind it for me? In the 1980s, it was not a run-of-the-mill career for a girl from a small town outside of Lancaster, Pennsylvania. The first question is often how did I even know this type of work and mission existed? Even today, many people have never heard of a specialty in the study of sexology.

For the answer, we need to go back to 1966 and my first job as a "tray girl" in our small-town hospital. "Tray girls" carried the evening meals to hospital patients. I saw a lot inside those hospital rooms. I saw the sick, the young dying, and the old. I traveled the hospital floors taking meals to the patients. Seeing their struggles and suffering affected me deeply and left a lasting impression that set me on a journey that has me writing to you today.

I remember the moment very clearly—standing in the hospital hallway, staring down at the food tray, making the decision that would later define my purpose. I would figure out how to avoid ending up there *and* find out how to help other people have relationships with their bodies as their best friends so they did not end up in a place like that, where there was such sickness, struggling, and suffering. That was the first step in my journey, which continues to this day and I plan to continue until I leave this body, which has been my best friend.

After graduating from high school in 1967, I went to my mother and told her I wanted to go to nursing school. "Girls don't go to college." Her response was typical of the thinking in that time. That was the end of my plans for nursing school for the time being. But I set out on a journey to find relevant classes and other sources of information, gathering available teachings on taking responsibility for your own health and wellness. It was a long time before the internet, so I did my research the old way. I looked in magazines and went to the local library to find books on food and diet. In the '70s the "New Age" movement was just getting started, with yoga, meditation, vegetarian diets, and other things we take for granted today. I was delighted to find a yoga class at the local YMCA! That still shocks me to this day. I was also able to attend a meditation class at a local church.

Books I found that are still well known include:

Diet for a Small Planet by Frances Lappe Moore

Living the Good Life by Helen and Scott Nearing and

Let's Eat Right to Keep Fit by Adelle Davis.

I also found the works of Dr. Herbert Shelton, who formed The Natural Hygiene Society which still exists today (http://www.naturalhygienesociety.org/).

I wanted and needed a religion or spiritual practice to

match my new exploration of how to stay well: body, mind, and spirit. I remembered that in high school there was a girl who was a Seventh-day Adventist. Adventists practiced a health message that included a vegetarian diet. I called her and asked for details about their health message. She said, "Come to church on Saturday." There, I gained the firsthand guidance and teachings I had been seeking regarding the connection between mind and body wellness. The parishioners gifted me with Ellen White's books on diet and health.

In 1980, as a Seventh-day Adventist, I studied at one of their healing sanctuaries, in Columbus, Georgia. The sanitarium is called Uchee Pines and is still a natural healing facility, utilizing a wide range of modalities for healing body, mind, and spirit. I spent the summer there and learned hydrotherapy, charcoal therapy, massage, and nutrition therapy—practices we see as mainstream and are accepted on a large scale now.

The church was my spiritual, as well as my mind-body wellness, family. We would purchase foods through mail order that were not readily available (as they are today), from the Adventist Organization's main location, Loma Linda, California. Monthly, we ordered tofu in twenty-five-gallon containers. We also ordered meat-substitute products such as Big Franks hot dogs, fake turkey burgers, and Chik Patties. We made trips to the Lancaster, Pennsylvania, Dutch countryside to purchase cantaloupes, corn, watermelons, and other farm-fresh seasonal fruits and vegetables. As a community, we either froze it, dried it, or canned it.

At home, I made our own cashew milk, sprouted grains, and yogurt. I acquired fresh local goat milk, which was continually fermenting in four little heating cups I kept on the kitchen counter. Today, when I go into even a small grocery store here, in our small town in Texas, I cannot believe there is an entire wall of yogurt in so many flavors and varieties. Now they carry almond-milk, soy-milk, and cashew-milk yogurt. I never could have imagined so much progress would happen in my lifetime.

I was put in charge of teaching the health message

in-house at the church and presented vegetarian cooking classes in the adult evening programs offered by the local schools. Keep in mind this was the early 1980s in small German-based communities in rural Pennsylvania! At that time, it was shocking that I would teach those classes and people would attend! Today, one of these towns has a vegan restaurant and a vegan grocery store, and almost every other restaurant in these towns has some vegetarian items on the menu. My community is an example of just how far the message has come over the years, even in small rural areas.

My dream of higher education was put on hold until 1985, when I found an ad for a position as secretary to the Dean of Men at Villanova University, located just an hour from my hometown. This position came with free tuition, which was a great help. I landed the job and began my career by enrolling in two classes per semester. I also continued teaching the health message and offering hands-on classes about the benefits of massage. I began teaching classes in gyms, and they were mostly attended by men. The concept of fitness centers emerged later, when women started to want locations to gather and work out.

This was also when aerobic classes began, and these were mostly for the girls. I provided hands-on therapy with "renegade" chiropractors who were on the cutting edge of this exploding industry. There was also a progressive hair salon, where I worked as their first massage therapist. It took seven years to complete my undergrad and to graduate cum laude with a Bachelor of Arts degree in human services.

While working my way through school as a massage therapist, I met two very progressive psychology and sexology therapists, Dr. Bill Stayton and Dr. Carol Cobb-Nettleton. They believed in the need to treat the mind and body for comprehensive wraparound mind-body wellness. To work toward "total wellness," we needed to include the body in a psychotherapy healing process. They had read Barbara Brennan's book *Hands of Light*. Her book began our understanding and acceptance of the use of life-force energy and hands-on therapy as tools for healing.

Eastern philosophies and various other religions continued to make their way across the oceans. Teachings that incorporated meditation, our entire diet, yoga, acupuncture, Reiki, shiatsu massage, and more had continued to spread across the states, mostly from California to the east. We were off to a movement for body-mind-spirit connection in all new ways.

A person still needed to know the "right" people and the current magazines—for example, *New Frontier Magazine* in Philadelphia—to be included in the network of the movement. At one time to attend a reflexology or tantra class, I had to drive at least an hour! At that time, the classes were scheduled sporadically and were not as openly available as they are for us today.

Dr. Stayton and Dr. Nettleton continued to provide an office for me in their counseling center, where I provided hands-on therapy to their psychology clients who were appropriate candidates for this intervention. I used hands-on approaches with folks who were struggling with living in their bodies. This can be related to the body being traumatized or violated or bodies that are confused. This included clients who felt they were in bodies that did not match their gender identities, men who wanted to wear lingerie during basic massage sessions, females and males struggling with and testing out cross-dressing or questions about transgender identity. We were just starting to delve into these types of cases in the late '80s and early '90s.

These clients and these questions sent me down the road to my interests and my need to understand how we can live more congruent lives in healthy bodies even when it gets more complicated. But it was not smooth sailing within the practice. There were therapists who left the center because I was doing touch therapy and working with "unique" clients, those with sexual orientations or gender identities that were unfamiliar to them. These individuals would now be described as bisexual, pansexual, or gender nonconforming; this hadn't been included in their psychological training. However, Dr. Bill and Dr. Carol and I were seeing miracles happening by incorporating touch therapy with talk therapy. Today, I call this neck-up (talk therapy) and neck-down (touch therapy) comprehensive mind-body wellness.

The **Masters and Johnson** research team, composed of William H. Masters and Virginia E. Johnson, pioneered research into the nature of human sexual response and the diagnosis and treatment of sexual disorders and dysfunctions from 1957 until the 1990s.

https://en.wikipedia.org/wiki/Masters_and_Johnson

Also, at this time, I was trained as a surrogate partner and began working for Masters and Johnson in St. Louis. This unique and precious opportunity validated the value of hands-on therapy in what is called the *triadic model* (therapist, touch practitioner, client). Talk about an adventure! The life-changing miracles! I knew I was on the right track and this therapeutic process was here to stay.

Upon graduating cum laude from Villanova, in 1992, with a BA degree in human services, I began my studies at the Institute for Advanced Studies of Human Sexuality in San Francisco. After completing their master's degree in Sex Education and their PhD in Sexology, I became a certified sexologist. Upon graduation, in the year 2000, I began to train massage therapists and other bodywork practitioners to provide touch therapy in conjunction with psychology professionals. These trainees formed a team approach, offering hands-on therapy for my sexology clients. Thus, we were providing both the neck-up and neck-down comprehensive mind-body wellness.

This training has grown now, into the business Integrative Mind-Body Therapies (IMBT) (https://imbtinternational.com/). At this writing, IMBT has nine teams around the country and growing as the somatic arts movement and integrative medicine become more mainstream, as the conscious diet, massage, yoga, and meditation did back in the 1960s and '70s. The return of these ancient somatic practices paved the way for the myriad of touch and talk modalities that we have available to us today.

These changes opened the field of bodywork in the 1980s by focusing on mental, emotional, and spiritual alignment. Borrowing a term from pioneering therapist Carl Rogers, they called this "congruence."

> *"Carl Rogers believed that for a person to achieve self-actualization they must be in a state of congruence. This means that self-actualization occurs when a person's 'ideal self" (i.e., who they would like to be) is congruent with their actual behavior (self-image)."*
>
> **Or as I call it, Plain Damn You!**
> *(https://www.simplypsychology.org/carl-rogers.html)*

Comprehensive wellness is ancient wisdom and statistically supported, beginning with researchers such as Ashley Montague in his book: *The Significance of the Human Skin*. This answers the question "how do we achieve comprehensive wellness of mind, body, and spirit?" To this day, I believe when the body and the mind are in alignment, we are in a place of congruency and connection to ourselves, which is the most important place to be. It is what aligns us to whatever we call spirit, source, joy, oneness... your call. Clearly, the experience is a deeper connection to being fully alive and engaged as our Creator intended.

As you read these pages, learn from others' journeys, observe the journey of "You with You," and revel in the possibilities of "You with Other."

Thirds Theory

of

Self-Actualization

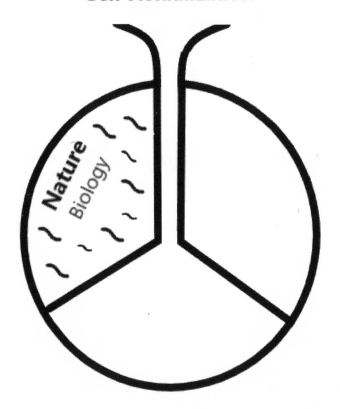

Chapter Two You with You

"You are the gardener that tends the garden called your body. Listen to your body, and it will tell you what you need to know." - Wayne Dwyer

When clients ask me, "Am I normal if...," I know they are referring to the "box" of what is "normal" today. The nature-nurture they were given, does it include or exclude them from others? What I have found they really want to know is "do I fit in" the rest of society? Do I measure up to its expectations in terms of looks, clothing, height, weight, the car I drive... etc. The pressure to be accepted and acceptable, to fit in, to be "normal" is, in most cases, the core of why they found me and picked up the phone.

You with You... is the most important question. It is what's natural for you as opposed to the "normal" or the "shoulds" that we are trained in, chided about, or even abused and forced to adhere to in our lives. Come walk with me on the journey of your life. Stop driving down the highway of your life with your eyes on the rearview mirror. This is the most important chapter... It is your chapter... Let's write it together.

~*~

In this chapter, I will walk you through the details I discuss with my clients when we begin our work together. It is the heart of discovering "Plain Damn You." To do that, we need to discuss some basic elements.

Our Session Begins

When a session begins, I welcome you and begin by letting you know how the session works. In the pages of the book, I'll take you through the types of information we discuss and need to delve into in a session. You can bring a notebook to keep notes if you want. The things that are mentioned in the book will likely stir ideas or memories, which can be helpful as you read the chapters, and making notes can be beneficial in discovering Plain Damn You. More details about that soon!

First, I add your name, email address, and phone number for the file. That makes it easier to communicate with you. I can also share that contact information if I pass your notes along to another team member in my network, as discussed below.

I need permission from you to take notes. If we deem it valuable for your process and if you agree, I will share the notes with other team members that we agree will be part of your treatment plan. I won't share any information with them without telling you. I want to make sure you understand this is my team approach depending on what *you and I* decide. Other people could be involved, either in the neck-up therapy part of your process or the neck-down part of the process. I'll add a note to your file that you have given me permission to take notes.

Depending on what's discussed, it may be appropriate to include others in your case. In that instance, they would review your notes, discuss your case with Dr. Susan, and consult with her after having a session with you. This guarantees each person involved with you stays up to date on your progress.

Next, I ask how you found me. Were you referred or did you hear about this work through a friend, another professional, a seminar, or some other way? I also want to know what motivated you to come to me. Why are you here? Why do you feel that you need my help?

These may not seem like very important questions, but they are. I especially need to know: What motivates you? And why do you feel you need my help? Those reach the heart of how I can help you, and your motivation is important. If you are in therapy to please someone else, but you think it is a stupid or bad idea, it will likely only be somewhat successful. If you truly want answers and you are determined to improve your situation, we can make major changes in your life. Do you see the difference?

We can talk during our first session, and I can answer

your questions. Understanding the process in more detail can help convince and motivate someone who is skeptical.

My next questions are simple information –

> ➤ How old are you?

> ➤ Do you live alone, or do you live with a partner or other people?

> ➤ Have you been married, and are you currently married?

> ➤ If you are married, how long have you been married?

> ➤ If you aren't married, are you in a relationship?

> ➤ If you are, how long have you been in the relationship?

> ➤ Is the relationship with a male or a female?

> ➤ Does your significant other know you are seeing me in a session?

> ➤ If you didn't tell them, is there a reason why not?

> ➤ Do you have children?

> ➤ If you have children, how old are they?

Understanding You with You

To begin, give me one snapshot of what you remember feeling and sensing up to about the age of five. We do not have cognition on board until about age six or seven. Before that, you are reading and understanding your whole world through your senses. Do you feel secure and safe? Do you feel abandoned? Do you feel loved?

> "The image is one thing and the human being is another... it's very hard to live up to an image."
>
> – Elvis Presley

These are some questions I would ask about your

very early life, to consider in your own notebook or journal, if you have one. Take some time to think about them. Make notes about each question and leave some space in case you think of something else that you want to add later.

> ➤ How were you raised, and what early messages did you get around your body and how to feel about it?

> ➤ What was your birth process? Were you born through a vaginal birth or a C-section? Were there complications?

> ➤ How were you handled in the hospital?

> ➤ Did you have health issues in the beginning that meant you had to spend more time with hospital staff than family?

> ➤ Did you bond right away with your mom or was there a reason you weren't held much?

> ➤ How was your early bonding with others?

> ➤ How were you handled from the neck down?

> ➤ What sort of messages did you receive through the age of five or six?

> ➤ How did you feel through your senses?

> ➤ What messages did you get through books that others read to you when you were very young, through touching, and through TV?

These are examples of how these early experiences can impact you later in life.

Cause	Effect
Felt like you were a burden	Feel unworthy of connection
Stayed behind in the hospital	Lack bonding and nurturing
Saw Mom and Dad fighting – could be verbal, physical, or both	Have stomach issues or anxieties
Mom was sick	Became her caretaker, became isolated
Dad was absentee, left with mom	Have unhealthy attachments
Molested by a family member or associate	Accept other abuse and don't speak up
Family abused alcohol and other drugs	Learned your needs don't matter
Were told your body was dirty, sinful, and evil	Struggle with dysfunctional relationships for years!

Each of these early chapters delves into your

personal history. I do this by using a template with each client. I take you through it and know exactly what I'm looking for in each topic. I try to do this in a timely manner, to get the information I need and discuss who on our team you will meet with next. It's different in the book because you can work through it at your own pace, and you have a wider array of details at your fingertips. But I wanted you to know how I work one-on-one.

Cellular and Body Memory

In addressing these body memories and cellular memories, we are removing these unknown blocks and traumas, early messages and stories that are stored within our bodies. These need to be cleared before you move on to You with Others. You must have a healthy You with You to have a healthy You with Others

Quote from Wikipedia:

Peter Levine calls BM (body memory) implicit

memory or, more specifically, procedural memory, things the body is capable of doing automatically and not in one's consciousness. He clarifies three types of BM and frames his work in terms of traumatic memory consequence and resolution:

1. Learned motor actions - Action patterns that can be continuously modified over time by higher brain regions.

2. Emergency response - Hardwired instinctual behaviors (i.e., fight or flight response, etc.).

3. Attraction or repulsion - We are attracted to sources of nourishment and growth and repulsed by sources of injury or toxicity.

Nicola Diamond elaborates on the opinion of philosopher Merleau-Ponty and asserts that BM is formed by doing, whether practicing a bodily activity or forming a reaction to a traumatic memory.

Edward Casey speaks of BM as "memory intrinsic to the body, how we remember by and through the body," rather than what is remembered about the body.

> *Thomas Fuchs defines six different types of BM: procedural, situational, intracorporeal, incorporative, pain, and traumatic memory. He notes that they are not strictly separable from one another but "derived from different dimensions of bodily experience. Michelle Summa further refines this definition as an implicit memory: a pre-thematic, operative consciousness of the past expressed through the body.*
>
> *Antonio Damasio calls these reactions to memories somatic markers, or emotions that are expressed primarily as physical feelings.*

Cellular or body memories need bodywork. When I first began hands-on therapy, back in 1985 at the offices of Dr. Bill Stayton and Dr. Carol Cobb Nettleton, I didn't really know what was happening between my touch and my client's response. This case that convinced all of us that we were on the right track is the story of a woman who had suffered chronic neck and shoulder pain since she could remember. By the time she was in her early thirties, the physical doctors had given up on treatments and had her meet with a therapist because her pain was not physical but was in her head. In other words, she (we will call her Kathy) was making up that she walked with a lifetime of pain in her neck and shoulders.

Kathy found her way to our office and met with Dr. Carol, who conducted a verbal intake to learn more about her childhood and any relevant events that had brought her to our offices, After the intake, Carol suggested that Kathy make an appointment with me for a bodywork session. A few days later, Kathy came into my massage room, fully clothed and lay facedown on the massage table. I began to move my hands over her back, then her shoulders, then her neck. She was on the table only about ten or twenty minutes and, as I rested my hands on her neck and shoulders she began to raise her arms up overhead while sobbing.

Today, I could tell you a thousand of these stories, but this was the one that convinced me, Dr. Carol, and Dr. Bill that we were on the right track. Cellular memories or body memories are real, and you cannot get to them by sitting across a desk and talking about them. This example is why bodywork, currently known as somatic arts, is core to the mind-body total wellness process.

How You Feel About You

An important part of You with You is how you feel about yourself and how you feel about sex and intimacy. That may sound funny but stick with me. Many things will influence your thoughts and feelings about sex, intimacy, yourself, and your body. We'll cover them in this book, and I cover them with each client. A big part of my work and the most important part of Plain Damn You is getting you to the best place possible, mentally, physically, and emotionally. The ultimate goal is for YOU to accept YOU sexually and intimately. Paramount in these first sessions are your feelings, thoughts, and beliefs. Building and understanding You with You is critical before we can take on You with Others.

When you see other people—they may be like you, or they may be different, being affectionate in public: kissing, hugging, or maybe a woman breastfeeding a baby in public—you have a thought or reaction. Did you ever think that how you bonded with your mother and how soon you bonded could impact how you react to seeing strangers hugging in public? All these thoughts and reactions are likely influenced by the material that will be explored in the next chapter.

Very strong opinions and teachings from our parents or grandparents can also affect us, depending on how close we were to them growing up. We will touch on this in the "You with Others" chapter but remember: all these things will affect you personally.

Reflections of You with You

   1. Recall a childhood smell memory. Was it

Grandma's chocolate chip cookies? Our sense of smell holds the most memories.

2. What is your first memory of touch? Was it being held while read to by a parent or sibling? Or being forced to hug or kiss old Aunt Hattie?

3. In reading through my intake description, what feelings or memories arise that could be interesting to think about or to discuss?

4. What would be your most interesting You with You behavior, and where did it come from?

Thoughts & Quotes

Body Image

Middle school for me was the worst. I entered sixth grade with a C cup and, in those days, it seemed huge. I hadn't asked to develop so much, but I had, and I wasn't exactly sure how to handle all the attention. The attention I ultimately received, however, was the type no one should ever have to handle.

Over the span of six months, I was harassed, degraded, and eventually molested daily, by a high school freshman. One of my neighbors called the police, and I came home that day to a driveway and yard full of police cars. They questioned me and, after speaking with the boy and his father (the mayor of the township), they decided it was my fault. My parents were told I encouraged this "fine, upstanding young man" and I was only trying to ruin his reputation and should be controlled better. No parent should ever be told that.

I carried around a lot of guilt after that. My mom and I talked about it, and I was given counseling at school daily. Slowly but surely, I realized the cops were wrong and no one asks to be molested. To this day I still hate the word, "molestation" because it brings up a lot of unhappy memories. But after a year or so of constant support, I made what they considered a full turnaround. I even spoke to other girls who had similar experiences to help them heal too.

~*~

Domestic Violence and Low Self-Esteem

Another problem is domestic violence, and I think a huge reason for that is the lack of education about gender roles and healthy relationships. Throughout history, males have been taught they were superior to women. This idea can be more present in the rural areas, where the quality of education may not rival urban areas. Most domestic violence cases go unreported because women accept their role and are either too scared or do not know any better. They grew up in that environment, like their mothers and their grandmothers before them.

Beginning to Heal a Damaged Body Image

While in California, I went to therapy with a behavioral scientist who helped me learn to love my body and appreciate it, no matter what shape or size, and never put it down. If I wasn't happy with the size and shape, I could change it. Since I lived alone, he suggested that I walk about my apartment completely naked to get used to being with my body unclothed and see my whole self, reflected in my mirrors, TV, and any other reflective surface. It was a freeing and very sensual experience, and I still use that as a tool to enjoy my body.

~*~

"Evidence shows that those who have been inadequately touched during their early years have not developed the ability to be psychologically touched." Ashley Montagu

~*~

"It appears that if we do not develop as tactile beings, we become insensitive to the needs of others." Susan Kaye Master's Thesis: Sensory Deprivation Effects on Personality 1998

~^~

If you don't love yourself, nobody else will. Not only that but you won't be good at loving anyone else. Loving starts with the self. Author Unknown

Chapter Three Early Messages

"The teaching model I use for all my clients is that of experiential education. My philosophy is that adults (and children) learn naturally, especially in the emotion-laden subjects of human sexuality and religion, when being part of the learning experience. We all learn from the great diversity of feelings about sexual material, different moral and ethical belief systems and the varied experiences of deeply held beliefs of members of our family." - William R Stayton MDiv, ThD, PhD

~*~

The early messages begin to form both You with You and You with Others. What if early messages about your body are of guilt, shame, fear? Or was the message "this is your precious body, the vehicle that takes you through life?" What we learn from our families' behaviors around living in a body and the messages we hear, feel, and absorb begin to set us up for the road we travel with our connection or disconnection to ourselves, our sensuality and sexuality.

This information is downloaded into your newly forming brain (thoughts) and body (feelings) and begins a thread of choices, events, and results that can be tracked to where you are today in relation to your body and the bodies of others. Let's take a walk down memory lane, the good and the not-so-good, to explore the "thread" that has shaped and formed you from the early messages, both in the neck up, to your mind, and the neck down, into the rest of the pieces of your own special jigsaw puzzle, called your body. This will help you see how I do my work and how you can understand why you "see" things the way you do. Let's begin!

When I first sit with a potential client and conduct an intake, I am looking at what messages were implanted and formulated in their early years. In these messages, I can track what I call the "thread" that brought them to me at age twenty-five, forty-five, sixty-five, etc. That thread carries the blocks to who you are as You with You and then shows up as who you are as You with Others.

I wish I had a dime for every client who has gasped when I said to them "do you see this early message and how it still has an impact on you?" This awareness gives them the hope and courage to confront these issues. The bravery and commitment to take this newfound determination and reach past these relationship blocks to forge ahead into You with Others.

~*~

We have talked about some aspects of our relationships with ourselves and how we begin to form our ideas, thoughts, and beliefs about things, including intimacy, relationships, and sex. We begin to form our thoughts about being close to others, being held, and reaching out for our parents and other loved ones as soon as we are born. Touch is a normal part of life, and we need it to thrive. When it is missing from our lives or is scarce, we notice. It may not register as that but, over time, it can change our behavior and expectations, which has an impact on us as we grow.

This is something we notice mostly as infants when we do not get touch from our caregivers. Even touch from our siblings and others makes a difference. What about medical touch when we were in the hospital? There have been reports that some hospitals started to rotate the placement of babies so they could all be closer to the nurses at times and get more attention. We are now more aware of the need for and value of skin touch.

There is a nationwide push called "rooming in." One example is Massachusetts, where some hospitals have eliminated their nurseries for well babies. The babies stay with their mothers around the clock to ensure their bonding, so the mother can breastfeed when needed, and for full education on how to care for her baby. The nurses get pushback from some mothers, who want rest and anticipated a "break" while their babies were in the nursery, but there are definite perks to this arrangement, far past just the few days in the hospital.

"Mothers and babies sharing a room is a key component of the "Baby-Friendly" initiative launched by the World Health Organization and the United Nations Children's Fund to encourage breastfeeding. US hospitals have been slow to adopt the program—for years, Boston Medical Center was the only hospital in Massachusetts to earn the "Baby-Friendly" label. But with the Centers for Disease Control pushing breastfeeding as a public health priority and the Joint Commission, a national accrediting organization, considering breastfeeding rates when it evaluates hospitals, hospitals are now ramping up."
https://www.bostonglobe.com/lifestyle/health-wellness/2016/02/06/nurseries/Ur4Xi846SPStbUx5PhxQtJ/story.html

I just want to mention a program that is doing a wonderful service for babies who are born addicted because their mothers took drugs while they were pregnant. This illustrates how powerful touch is at a very young age. When the baby is born, they go through withdrawal from whatever drug their mother was taking, just like an adult would. The nurses who care for them have said that when they are held and cuddled for extended periods, they are able to deal with the withdrawal symptoms better. So, people volunteer to come in and cuddle these babies to help them through this ordeal. You can read more about their work here – https://uplift.love/the-drug-affected-newborns-being-healed-through-touch.

Digging Into Early Relationship Messages

Let's start with your life up till the age of about five to seven. At this point, you do not have discernment cognition. Say your parents are fighting with other people in the house or fighting between themselves. When you are at that age, you do not have the ability to understand their argument is not your fault. You do not yet have the mental capacity to determine it is between them and their relationship. They need to work it out between themselves; it does not involve you.

As a child, you live through your senses and your sensuality. Your sensuality includes how you feel. Two big parts of that include whether you feel secure or insecure and whether you feel loved or not loved. Do you feel responsible for things that happen around you? As a child, you are a "sensual" computer. Your "download" is registered and recorded through the smells, the sounds, the visuals, and the sensations that follow you through mental or cellular memory. When upsets or trauma occurs, this can lead you to assume the blame. For example, you believe that your parents are fighting because of something you did. This is a guilt many children needlessly carry with them for years.

When I work with clients, I look at the first fourteen years. First, I want you to think back and tell me who raised you. During that time, did you feel loved, taken care of, and nurtured? Or was there neglect, abuse, or trauma during those years? Another important element is to know if you felt the people who were in charge loved one another, were nurturers, and were affectionate with each other. All these things form your early relationship messages and create the foundation for what you believe about relationships later in life.

When clients nonchalantly say, "things were good" I ask, what does "good" look like to you? What do you mean when you say that? Describe "good" or "bad" from your perspective. Each person's view of "good" or "bad" is different, so explain what that means to you and what it meant in your childhood. What you are saying is that "your normal felt good" to you. Paint a picture for me of your home and your family when you were a child so I can see what you mean.

Remember to get out your notebook and make notes about these answers. These answers will give you insights into your perspectives about relationships. Any time I include questions for you, to get ideas, throughout the book, it would be good to make notes so you can go back and take a look at them later and to help you think about your own life. It is amazing what we can remember and discover.

Here are some things to consider and to include in your description. Were there any major changes for you or your family during this time? A common change in families is the addition of siblings, which adds a whole new dynamic. If you had brothers and/or sisters, did that change your relationship with your mother or father? Did you feel like you had been replaced? Did you get along with your sibling(s)? Did the addition of sibling(s) cause problems in the household? That can be a very involved answer in some families.

We get these early relationship messages mainly from the people who raised us, who are usually our parents. They might be other family members. They can also be close family friends, neighbors, our parents' coworkers, parents of close friends, or others that we spent a lot of time around. Are there other people that you were around a lot as a young child that had a big impact on you?

Older siblings and cousins you spent time around can also have an impact on you. The family's church community can also leave a big and lasting impression, which we will discuss in a later chapter. Did you have cousins that lived close when you were young? Older relatives that are close to your age can affect what you learn about the opposite sex and about your own sexuality and relationships, dating, and so much more at a very young age. Through no fault of their own, much of the information you learned from them at that age was often not entirely true, because they had not yet learned the facts either.

What kind of messages did you get from your parents and your place of worship, if you attended one, about relationships? Were parents expected to be married and children to live with both parents? Or did your parents get divorced when you were young? If so, how did this affect your view on relationships and family? All these early basics set up your frame of reference for what is "normal."

How Early Are Early Messages?

Your early sex messages are critical to your sexual

development, and that influence starts much earlier than you likely imagine. The way your parents treated you and bonded with you—or did not bond with you— can impact your relationships later in life. That is why we started by discussing those very early interactions between you and the people who raised you. Whether you stayed in the hospital or went home with your parents right away also impacted those early days and the initial stages of bonding with your mother and father and bonding with any siblings. Do not underestimate the importance of those very early days and the things that happened to you and around you. Even if you do not think you remember them, your body does.

Let's consider the sexual messages that might have been conveyed to you. These early sexual messages start to formulate in many ways and before we are aware of it. Many things that happen as we are growing up can affect how we perceive ourselves, our bodies, our feelings, and our curiosities and concerns as we begin to explore this new and mysterious world.

To get you thinking, here are some questions to consider:

➢ Did your parents or guardians talk about your body?

➢ How did they talk? Was it positive or negative?

➢ Did adults shy away from talking about your body and, in particular, your genital area and sexuality?

➢ Was sexuality a topic that was discussed in the home?

➢ Was guilt and shame associated with talk of bodies or sex?

➢ Did adults talk about bodies, sex, and sexuality like they were "dirty"?

➢ How did your parents act or react if there was any mention of sex by you, on TV, or by anyone else in the house?

➢ If talk about sex was avoided, did that make you feel more positive or negative about it?

➢ When sex was mentioned, did your parents also talk about God and religion?

➢ Was there talk about marriage, sanctity, and purity?

Each person has their own unique upbringing and experience. As we are discussing in this book, we each have our own perspective on what we feel is "normal." How our caregivers talk about and handle sexual topics will vary. It may be a little bit or very different from other people that we know. When you were very young, it's likely you did not have enough information to notice sexual messages. But when we're older, we may look back on some behaviors, incidents, events, or situations and be more sexually curious about what was said, what we heard, or what we experienced. It would not be unusual to see these things in a very different light as an adult.

For example, if you were in your parents' bedroom, got into their nightstand, and found a *Playboy* magazine, a porn video, condoms, a jar of Vaseline, or a vibrator and they saw you, they were most likely embarrassed but, at the time, that confused you. Some parents would holler at their children if this happened, while others would quietly take the items and hide them. A few who decided to be open with their children would explain what these items were, in a way that was appropriate for the child's age. Depending on the child's questions, the explanation may be brief or more detailed. This incident could be something you would not remember if you were shamed for it, but years later when I saw you, you might feel guilty but not understand why.

When clients come for their first appointment with me, they usually begin by saying, "I had a "normal" childhood." They often say nothing unusual happened when they were growing up. Some have blocked out sexual messages that occurred before about the age of twelve or thirteen. That is the age we generally become more aware of our sexuality and sensuality. This is when our peers begin reporting experiences and noticing changes in their bodies and forming attractions. However, our minds and our bodies have been taking notes and forming memories long before that time. Even though you are not aware of them, these early messages are influencing your physical, mental, and emotional behaviors; opinions; fears; and desires involving sex and relationships. This applies most of all to your relationship regarding You with You and your relationships regarding You with Others, which we will discuss more later. These early messages are the beginning of how you decipher what you consider "normal" or "not normal" for *you*.

"Long ago, I was three or four and was playing with my Barbie and Ken dolls with a friend. I laid Ken on top of my naked Barbie. My mom walked in and yelled when she saw the dolls and she sent my friend home."

She remembered this decades later and thought about it at the strangest times—for example, when she undressed. Even when she was alone, she pulled something up to hide parts of her naked body. That's an example of early sexual messages our parents can give us without realizing the lasting effects. Her mother did not say it was wrong, but her behavior made her daughter feel it was wrong and made her feel ashamed. How many things like that do you think we have hidden away?

"The Talk"

The most common way we form our early impressions about sex is how we first find out about sex. This is true whether the messages come from our parents, caregivers, friends, other family members, school, magazines, religion, or the internet. It's not just *where* we hear these messages, but also *how* they are presented.

Often these messages about our bodies and sex come along with a heavy dose of shame and guilt. This is unfortunate for many reasons. One reason is because these messages can come when we are vulnerable and unable to form our own opinions, and it can take a long time to undo that damage. Sadly, some people are not able to find their "truth," or they travel a road of disconnection and loneliness until they reach out and seek support and guidance. I wish I had a dime for everyone who has said to me, "I've never told anyone this before."

One day I posed a question on my Facebook page asking people to share how their parents handled "the talk." These are some ways their parents or caregivers handled "the talk" with them –

- Parent handed the child a book or booklet and said to read it on their own.

- Parent got a book and read it along with the child.

- Parent had a talk of some kind with daughter when her period started.

- Parent handed daughter a pad when her period started with little or no talk.

- Parent told the child to ask their older siblings or cousins.

- Parent said to ask their friends.

- Parent said nothing and ignored questions.

- Parent said the school would tell them

- Parents got angry when asked about sex.

- Parents sent the child to their grandparents for information.

Do you notice a trend in these responses? They are not helpful, and they are not positive steps to start you off with information and an understanding of this basic human experience called sexuality. Often, these messages have a negative impact on your views about your body and sexuality as you grow into your teen, adult, and relationship years. Ambiguous, hurtful, and silent messages can, and often do, create shame and/or guilt because it was clear, from the way they reacted, that your caregivers had issues and concerns with the topic. Most of these messages are passed down from generation to generation. Parents, family, and friends only know what they were told, unless we take it upon ourselves to question, explore, educate ourselves, and become our own self-actualized adults. Otherwise, we will always be the product of the early sex messages they passed on to us. That will cause us to always be searching and questioning and lamenting over "Am I normal if...?"

Without saying anything directly, they are conveying the message that sex is something to be hidden or not talked about. This is what I call the 10 percent of our anatomy that is considered shameful and should not be discussed or understood. We are expected to simply overcome desires that are normal and natural but some people feel are either a mistake or a test from our creator. Otherwise, our parents, our teachers, our ministers, our siblings, our guardians, our doctors... would answer your questions, wouldn't they? Have you heard the saying "often it's not about what is said, but what isn't said?" Many times, we learn more from what people don't say than what they do say, even if we do not realize it at the time. Often, we also learn more about other people and their hang-ups from their behavior than from what they say.

The same was true when you were young and your parents shut off certain TV programs when you walked in the room. Or when your dad hid the *Playboy* magazine or *Hustler*. He was teaching you that the body was a bad thing. With advances in technology, now it is done by shutting the laptop or switching the computer screen away from a porn site.

Something that has been very encouraging over the years, while interviewing clients, is when parents reported that they made a point of being more open with their children because of how badly their parents handled "the talk" or because they didn't handle it at all. My clients made sure to talk with their children and let them know they could come to them with questions. One woman mentioned she knew her daughter had already heard the details from friends and school, but she talked with her anyway. She did this because it opened the lines of communication between them about sexuality and let her daughter know it was alright to come to her mom with questions in the future. What an enlightened and caring mother.

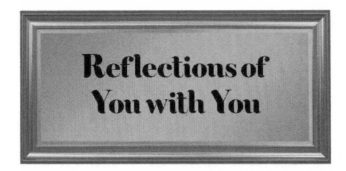

1) What is your favorite body part? Least favorite? Why?

2) If there is a memory thread that begins in childhood and is still affecting you in adulthood, what would it be?

3) Were early sex messages negative or positive? Which ones do you remember the most?

4) Is shame one of the blocks to your relationship connecting You with You? If so, how does that affect you?

Thoughts and Quotes –

Common messages were that girls who had sex were sluts and guys who didn't have sex were weak. I got messages that heterosexuality was the only type that was acceptable and the only type that was talked about with even a semblance of a positive attitude.

The first time I can recall even bringing up the topic of sex was when I was maybe six or seven. I dressed my Barbie in a bathing suit and a dress and had her do a little strip show in front of my parents, hoping for their approval. Obviously, that didn't go over well. They were in shock for a few minutes, then they told me over and over that it was a bad grown-up thing and not to do it again. Before this happened, I didn't know it was bad. I thought it was just something weird that adults did on TV. After that my parents were more careful to tell me what was sexual and what was not.

~*~

There was one situation when I was thirteen that I'll never forget. I was getting ready for school one morning and while in the bathroom I got my period. My mother came in the bathroom, told me how to put the pad on, and let me stay home from school. That was all she did. Looking back, I find it kind of strange that she never explained what was going on with my body. I always knew I would get my period, but I never really understood why and about the changes with my body.

~*~

We discussed sex and its many taboos openly in our home. My father was a police officer, and no child of his was going to walk into the world not knowing the dangers of the world. School was for education, church was for religion, and sex education was taught in the home. There were no exceptions. Our open discussions were the result of what my dad couldn't forget when he came home at night. It puts a different spin on how you get raised when you are the daughter in a long line of cops.

In fifth grade they split the boys and the girls up and we separately watched some videos about the girl and boy reproduction organs. The videos were filled with information regarding pregnancy, diseases, etc. What I did as a naïve and ignorant child was go straight home and check for all of those diseases that were discussed in the video. While examining myself I saw little bumps (normal) and I freaked out and immediately thought it was herpes. I know now it was impossible to have herpes without any sexual contact with another. I went straight to my mom and asked if I could show her something. We went into my room, locked my door, pulled down my pants and I asked her if what I was seeing was herpes. She asked me if anyone had ever touched me there and I said no.

She laughed and assured me it wasn't herpes. We then had a discussion on how those things could happen and how to prevent it. I'm pretty sure my mom had nightmares that night. I don't think she planned to have that conversation so early.

~*~

I had the whole sex education thing in fifth grade where all the girls went in one room and all the boys went into another and we watched our separate movies. I always thought they should let us switch videos so we could learn all of it—well all they were willing to share with our impressionable young minds. The teachers seemed terrified to answer questions we had, and we were sent from the rooms, supposedly knowing all we needed to know about sex.

~*~

I was never free to talk with my mom about sexual issues. I was raised in a totally Catholic family where premarital sex was still a sin and thinking dirty was not an option. My mom would never tell me anything besides you have to be a virgin for your husband, but I never shared this idea. I believe marriage is more than love and it's necessary to have a sexual connection with the person you're going to be spending a lot of your life with and if that doesn't exist, there will be cheating.

When I was about eleven, Mom ordered a package from a maxi pad company. It came in a green box, and it had maxi pads and a little booklet. We went outside and lay in the sun and read the little booklet. I was so embarrassed because I knew the older man next door could hear us. We finished reading and she asked if I had any questions, and I didn't dare ask any questions. No, none. Then we went back in the house and we put the box under my bed and she said when I was ready and needed them, just let her know. I was like, oh please don't let me ever need them. About a year and a half later, I needed them.

One morning in the middle of seventh grade English

class I had a really bad stomachache, but I ignored it and went to school anyway. During class I noticed my underwear was wet. In my naivete, I believed that I had peed my pants, so I trotted out to the bathroom to assess the damage. Luckily when I spotted the blood everywhere, I came to the conclusion that I was not bleeding to death but was having a period. That's where my luck ended. Instead of having someone call my mom, I made a roughshod pad out of toilet paper and returned to class as if nothing had happened. You can imagine what happened next.

Early development: "Indeed, to a very significant extent, a measure of the individual's development as a healthy human being is the extent to which they are freely able to embrace another and enjoy the embraces of others. The tactually failed child grows into an individual who is not only physically awkward in their relations, but also psychologically and behaviorally awkward." Ashley Montagu

Chapter Four Religion

"A positive Christian message about sexuality and our sexual, sensual bodies is desperately needed. We do very destructive things when we are cut off from our bodies' treasure and when we limit pleasure. A rush to war, domestic violence, and aggressive relationships are all related to our comfort level to the body and to our lack of access to pleasure." Rev. Dr. Beverly Dale

Wikipedia describes "religion" as an organized collection of beliefs, cultural systems, and worldviews that relate humanity to an order of existence. In Hebrew: religion can be described as a set of laws. In Latin: sense of right, moral obligation, fear of the gods.

Whatever religious training we received as children had something to do with belief systems, laws, morality, and fear. As a budding teenager, young adult, and even adult, these messages were ingrained in your fiber both neck up and neck down. What was right, proper, acceptable before the eyes of the church, your elders, and mostly a Supreme Being. These teachings often conflicted with what we were feeling, struggling with, and making decisions about during the years when we were developing emotionally, mentally, and physically and as our characters were forming. In this chapter, we acknowledge that each of us has our own story. Some serve us well and others confuse and confine us in the journey toward healthy sexuality and lasting joy and happiness.

~*~

Religion can be a touchy and very personal topic for people, whether they are religious or not. In this chapter, my goal is not to judge anyone's beliefs or values in any way. My goal is to inform and educate my readers about the impact that religion, the things we are taught, and the beliefs of the people around us can have on our lives. These early childhood messages can and do affect our relationships, our perceptions of our bodies, our sexuality, and much more throughout our lives.

The messages that we receive affect us, whether we realize it or not. The following table contains examples of some of these causes and the effects they can have on us. There are many more examples.

Cause	Effect
Prayers to God because of shame and guilt over masturbation	Pre-ejaculation for men, rushing to finish masturbation for men, inability to orgasm for women
Guilt over thinking about and wanting to have sex	Anxiety, stress, and the need to be medicated
Having gone to a different church with each parent and having been told by parents that each other's religion is bad	Mental and physical concerns. Also stress and conflict with parents and other family members.

Women being forced to be submissive and being disrespected	Lower self-esteem, lower self-confidence, talents and abilities remain unrecognized. Family dysfunction
Being taught that genitals and pleasure are bad, dirty, and evil	Inorgasmic – unable to orgasm
Sex before marriage or getting pregnant – violating the rules of the church	Being removed from the church, thrown out of the home, or chastised by the church. Losing touch with family and friends
Religious authority figures misusing their positions sexually	Abuse, trauma, marital issues, secrets, stress, anxiety, etc.

The messages we absorb about sexuality and sensuality can seem nonexistent or can be very confusing for many people throughout the preteen and teen years. For some people, that may not improve in our early twenties and beyond. This can be particularly true for people who grew up in especially strict and/or religious homes.

Some young people, and some people who are older,

do not have anyone to talk openly and honestly with about relationships, love, and sex. Many of them have questions or struggle with confusion. Maybe the person is a church member, and they think it would be a good idea to speak with their pastor. Or maybe the person is a teen that is involved in a church youth group or a church camp, and they talk to a counselor or their youth pastor. I have heard of only a few denominations and select religious leaders who handle these questions in a healthy and positive way. More often than not, their answers and the tone of their responses paint sex and intimacy in a negative, "dirty," and shameful way. I will explain in more detail what I mean throughout this chapter.

Message Delivery Has Lasting Repercussions

People in religious households often hear messages about purity, chastity, and the sin of desire. Messages that sex before and/or outside of marriage are wrong and not approved by God are very common. Another is that sex is for procreational purposes only: for the purpose of getting pregnant and having a baby. Something to reflect on if you struggle with these early messages is how they were delivered, and by whom, and how they were received as a developing child. Also... do these messages now fit into your quest, as an adult, for You with You?

As we work through the search for *Plain Damn You*, remember we want to determine if various things "serve you." When you were a child, your parents and your preacher taught you what *they* felt you needed in your life, what *they* felt you needed to know. That likely mirrored their personal belief systems. Now that you are older, and since this book is about discovering the things that affect you from your childhood, let me share something shocking with you. The belief system that was so important to your parents very likely *will not be exactly the same for you*. There may be many core similarities, but you should not feel bad or guilty when you find that your life and your happiness include some different ideas and beliefs. It is up to you whether you explain those differences to family and friends. For now, let's focus on finding what does serve you (work for you in your life) and what does not serve you (does not work for you). You can make decisions about communicating those details later on. These are very personal and intimate decisions and are *your* decisions. It is not up to anyone else to make them for you! Figuring it out, finding the things that serve you, and making these changes are our first priority!

Body messages are often delivered in a negative way and often have the effect of creating a lot of shame around the topic of sexuality. We should also be able to feel self-confident in our bodies, without the usual "am I normal if..." about our bodies. Sex can and should be a very natural part of life. We are sexual beings, and that is a natural part of a healthy and loving relationship that begins with ourselves then spills over to others. It can and should be for procreation as stated in Genesis 9:7, where we were told to go forth and multiply. Sex is required to have children (procreation). The Bible also discusses sexual pleasure, in the Song of Solomon 7:8: "I will climb the palm tree and take hold of its fruit. May your breasts be like clusters of grapes and the fragrance of your breath like apricots." Both biblical messages about the body should be recognized and honored as natural and normal regarding our sexual well-being.

> The teaching that sex is only for procreation can cause many problems for people who are LGBTQIA, postmenopausal, or losing testosterone; men and women who have a wide variety of medical conditions that prevent pregnancy; and couples who choose not to have children.

Shame and Guilt Is Not Resolved

What happens in a relationship when one of the partners has a negative view of sex? What if they feel ashamed or guilty during sex? This is far more common than many people realize, and often it can be traced back to a strict religious upbringing and messages they received when they were younger. It can also be common for a family to talk about the duties or obligations connected to sex. These messages could be delivered as jokes or seriously, but the harm is still done, and without the correct education and information, partners are at a loss as to how to communicate or connect. These things combine to create a fear in the partner that, in some cases, may never be resolved and can cause many intimacy issues throughout the relationship.

Shame can be associated with anything pertaining to sexuality, sensuality, and the natural desires of the human body, especially the female breasts and the genital areas (referred to as "down there"). It can make us feel guilty for thoughts about sexuality, questions about our bodies, and the desire to know more. We all came into the world through our mothers' bodies, but many people are unwilling or unable to openly discuss bodies and sexuality, or talk about it only in limited ways. This is where the problems start. When people make so many things seem negative or forbidden, and add shame and guilt, there can be long-term disconnecting.

These long-term impacts are rarely addressed or even acknowledged by religion. When someone mentions them, they are ignored or glossed over. When a lack of sensual or sexual connection in a relationship starts to pile one brick on top of the other, creating a wall between partners, many couples do not understand what happened or why it is happening to them. That's a problem that can create a lifetime of relationship struggles.

Consider a teenage woman who has been brought up with strong messages that any sort of kissing, petting, fondling, or other intimacy is wrong. Her mother hasn't told her anything aside from scant details about her period and that, at the right time, she will be married. Then she will do her "wifely duty" and have children. She is told that a "good Christian woman" doesn't enjoy this, but it is her duty to produce children. Often a young woman has been sheltered and is understandably scared on her wedding night. She doesn't have any details, and if she was set up in a marriage of convenience, she may barely know her new husband. This is more common than people know, due to organizations such as Purity Culture. Imagine she marries a young man, or even a more mature man, who knows or cares very little about pleasing a woman. She may never learn any real details about her personal sexuality, even in the 2020s. She may also carry shame and guilt, even once she's married, because there was no real segue from being taught to feel guilty about her sensual body to marriage, in which she has no new information.

Gay, transgender, and bisexual folks are also brought up with strong messages that the only acceptable option is a heterosexual union that produces children. This focus on sex for procreational purposes only eliminates and demonizes all other options for loving, sharing, and enjoying our bodies for the pleasure for which we were designed.

The clitoris has 8,000 nerve endings! Touch is our most developed sense when we are born. We do not hear so well or see so well, nor have taste buds. We can only smell mothers' milk in the beginning. But our entire "skin bag" is fully on board with all the nerve endings we will have until death. What happens as we age out? We can't see so well, hear so well, we lose our sense of taste and smell, but our skin hungers for touch, and that never changes unless we have an accident or illness. God did not make a mistake in the design of our skin. It hungers for and desires healthy, safe, consensual sexual and sensual connections.

Enjoying or Not Enjoying Sex

Most of us know people—whether it be ourselves, friends, or family members—who simply do not enjoy sex. Some of the reasons may be:

- Do not understand the basics about sex

- Do not understand how the body works

- Do not understand what would or could "satisfy" us

- Feel shame or guilt about being satisfied

- Feel guilt and shame about being interested, or even being curious

- Experience guilt and shame for being excited

and "turned on"

- Will not or cannot become vulnerable and enjoy sex with a partner

- Did not learn how to enjoy or interact in a sexual way—have limited knowledge

- Feel too much guilt and shame about sex to be with someone

- May have unaddressed or unresolved sexual trauma

These are all common reasons that people have for not enjoying sex. They are common reasons that people from strict upbringings give for not having sex or having a difficult time with enjoyable sex when they are also struggling with guilt and shame from a strict background. It is a tough thing to deal with and makes it hard to even learn more about ourselves, our bodies, and what we want and need in our relationships. Often there is no real explanation or education about sex, your body, intimacy, the emotions, and so much more. That is a big leap— emotionally, mentally, and physically—to make all at once with no support or assistance.

Abstinence Only

Something that is often recommended or pushed by parents and/or churches is abstinence-only sexual education. They say, "Don't teach or talk about sex or they will do it." However, there is the opposite idea about drug usage: talk to your kids, teach them about drug use so they won't do it. Some states have abstinence-only sex ed, but fewer states are doing this in 2021.

What is sexual abstinence?

Sexual abstinence or sexual restraint is refraining from some or all aspects of sexual activity for medical, psychological, legal, social, financial, philosophical, moral or, most often, for religious reasons.

When many young people in religious homes are growing up, their pastors and parents make it very clear there is no choice. They are to remain abstinent and be virgins until they are married. I think we all know that does not necessarily mean it happens, and their parents and pastors do not always find out any differently.

There are some definite issues with abstinence-only sex education. The parents want to encourage their children to remain chaste and "save" themselves for marriage. However, many are not preparing them for a loving, intimate relationship in marriage, and they are not giving them the intimate education they need as they become healthy, sensual adults. Here are some pros and cons to abstinence.

Pros to Abstinence

- Abstinence is the only 100 percent effective form of pregnancy prevention.

- There is no chance of sexually transmitted diseases.

- Teens who are abstinent are less likely to be in abusive relationships or be pressured into having sex. Less likely but both can happen.

- Abstinent teens in romantic relationships do not worry their partners are only with them for sex.

- Some studies show couples are happier when they wait to have sex until they are more serious or are married.

- Teens are more vulnerable at their age, and sex can cloud their judgment. Waiting till they are older can be a wise move.

- Having sex early can cause lower self-esteem and make a person less self-reliant.

- Waiting till later to have sex can help teens build more solid relationships based on more solid foundations.

- Studies have shown that abstinent teens report, on average, better psychological well-being and higher educational attainment than those who are sexually active. Delaying the initiation of or reducing early sexual activity among teens can decrease their overall exposure to risks of unwed childbearing, STDs, and psycho-emotional harm. Authentic abstinence programs are, therefore, crucial to efforts aimed at reducing unwed childbearing and improving youth well-being. (Download the full report here https://www.heritage.org/education/report/evidence-the-effectiveness-abstinence-education-update)

- Abstinence is free and there are no side effects like you could have with some forms of birth control.

Cons to Abstinence

- Men and women often end abstinence without a plan to protect against pregnancy or sexually transmitted infections or diseases.

- Long-term abstinence can affect a person's self-esteem, especially if one person is repeatedly being rejected and the other is always being pressured for sex.

- Scare tactics used to pressure anyone into repressing sexual feelings can have a psychological impact on the development of a person's sexual and sensual self.

- While people may want to avoid abusive relationships, they may not learn how to spot a potential abusive relationship—including the signs of a potential abuser. Or they may get wrong or confusing information combined with abstinence information.

- Some people hide behind religious objections to avoid intimacy for a variety of personal reasons. Some reasons include:

  - fear, guilt, and shame
  - lack of social skills

- lack of knowledge about sex and intimacy
- having been taught, or feeling, that bodies are the gateway to sin

• Sex is emotionally bonding, and people tend to feel an emotional closeness when they have sex.

• Some people prefer masturbation, as many women say they orgasm better through masturbation, especially younger women who are having sex with inexperienced young men.

• Unfulfilled desire and peer pressure to have sex can be a vicious, confusing, and frustrating cycle.

• Having sex regularly protects the heart, lowering the risk of heart attack in men. For both men and women, it increases blood flow to the genitals and potentially helps the immune system.

Sex and Pregnancy Outside of Marriage

Young men and women usually get two different versions of the "don't get pregnant" talk. If the conversation is had, girls are told "don't get pregnant," and boys are told "don't get a girl pregnant." The easiest way for that to be "avoided" is to not have sex outside of marriage, and that is the preference in religious households. This is often an unrealistic option and most likely does not include any discussion, just an order, often accompanied by a threat.

These parents seem to ignore the important fact that it is hard for their children to know how to be safe. Sometimes a young person knows so little about sexuality that they can get into a dangerous situation and have no idea what's happening to them. They can also be taken advantage of in many ways—emotionally, mentally, and physically—by people who have more sexual information. If they do have sexual contact with a person, how can they avoid sexually transmitted diseases or pregnancy if they don't have any knowledge about their body or their sexuality?

The story of "Amy" comes to mind. Her father had a

frightening way of teaching his daughter to be safe and not to get pregnant. He said, "If you get pregnant, I will throw you down the stairs in hopes that the baby dies." She didn't know how pregnancy happened. She knew kissing and touching were taboo because they could lead to the mystery of pregnancy, but she was confused about how that made a baby.

Various religions handle reproduction in different ways, but the result is mostly universal. Your parents, the minister, and God will all be disappointed if you engage in this "unholy" or "dirty" act outside the sanctity of marriage. Shame and guilt are a big part of this scenario, and some religions have severe consequences for sex and pregnancy outside of marriage. What I call late-life virgins come to me with the most heartbreaking stories of loneliness due to avoiding connection and relationships because of these teachings.

Another client, Jennifer, who as a young girl attended a friend's sleepover party, heard a message that affected the rest of her life. Alone in sleeping bags on the living room floor, the girls began to talk and giggle about boys, kissing and having babies. One of the girls said that to get a baby, a boy has to pee inside you. Jennifer never forgot this and, to this day, that misinformation was her mental picture of what occurred during intercourse.

Even if your parents didn't have "the talk" with you, they likely did say something about not getting pregnant or not getting someone pregnant. This is usually accompanied by threats or scare tactics of some type. The type of tactics depends on the family and their beliefs, values, and background. We all know families who have had daughters get pregnant and sons who got their girlfriends pregnant. Some of these families throw their children out of the house; others help them to varying degrees. Some parents help even if they initially threatened to abandon their children in the event of an unplanned pregnancy. When faced with the actual situation, they changed their minds. But other parents followed through on their threats. I am sure there are people reading this book who had each experience or know people who have.

For those of us that faced conversations with parents, guardians, friends, etc. and had pregnancy scares as teens, even if these scares were false alarms, those memories leave scars. That is especially true in very religious and strict families.

Unintended Pregnancies and Lack of Sex Education

Very few parents *want* their teen daughters to end up pregnant and alone. However, they sometimes make decisions that put them more at risk of having that happen, without knowing it. This can happen when parents don't talk to them about "the facts of life" and their children get insufficient sex education. This can happen when parents choose to focus only on abstinence education and avoid actual sex education.

This has been supported by surveys and statistics. Parents run the risk of having their children end up in situations they are not prepared for because they did not get any sex education, because they were only trained NOT to have sex. Some people, even with the intentions of being abstinent, choose to engage in some sort of intimate activities, and they do not know how to handle the feelings that arise or things that happen.

This lack of sex education can also leave young people vulnerable to advances by predators who would take advantage of their lack of knowledge. We want to protect our children, but to protect them, they need to understand what to be on the lookout for and how to be aware. They need education and the ability to make safe, wise, and *informed* decisions. A person may be attacked or assaulted by someone and be unprepared to know *how* to deal with the situation. They could be unaware of what has even taken place, as unlikely as that may sound to some people.

Purity Culture

In the 1990s, the evangelical purity movement was born, and it is still alive today. Millions have read

Joshua Harris's Christian cult classic, *I Kissed Dating Goodbye* to learn the nuts and bolts of the culture. People who have been in the culture often say false promises, misinformation, shame, and fear are used to get people to abstain from sex. That makes sense; for centuries, many religions have used shame, guilt, and fear to manipulate people into doing what they want.

Myths About the Purity Culture

These are from an article online about how to provide an overview of the ideas being perpetuated in the purity culture and the writer's perspective on these ideas.

Spirituality Barometer Myth – A person's virginity is considered a measure of their faith. A believer's sexual history is the primary mark of their spiritual status. Church members are judged on whether they are "good Christians" based on their "purity." Rather than knowing Christians by their relationship with Jesus, purity culture asserts *that we will know them by their virginity*.

Fairy Tale Myth – As long as a young woman waits to have sex, *God will provide a wonderful husband that will fulfill all the items on the lengthy checklist she has created for a perfect husband.* Turning God into her Fairy Godfather.

Flipped Switch Myth – Young Christians are told to *stay chaste until their wedding night, and automatically a "switch will be flipped" and they will immediately have an incredible sex life.* Note: That's not how it works.

Damaged Goods Myth – People are reminded that they are considered *damaged goods if they have sex before marriage.* They are bringing a "defiled body" to their wedding night. This is ridiculous and *we are worthy of healthy, loving, and caring relationships whether we are virgins on our wedding nights or not. I would recommend being honest with your fiancé.*

Women Are Gatekeepers Myth – Purity culture is rooted in patriarchal theology and traditional gender roles. According to this theology, *women are asexual and don't want or enjoy sex as much as men. Sex is primarily to meet men's sexual needs and urges, and women should perform their "wifely duties" cheerfully, willingly, and enthusiastically. Purity culture claims that all men have high sex drives, can't help but sexualize women, and can't control themselves or be held responsible for their sexual desires. Because women are, apparently, less sexual, they are expected to be gatekeep of their men's sexuality.*

The Myths of Purity Culture are part of the article that was published at this site:

https://www.cbeinternational.org/resource/article/mutuality-blog-magazine/5-purity-culture-myths-and-why-they-are-false-promises

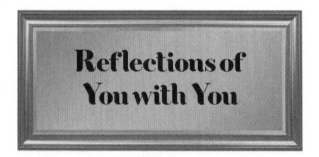

Reflections of You with You

1) Do religious teachings inhibit a positive relationship with your own body? How could you improve that relationship?

2) Could your religious teachings give you respect

in relating to other bodies? If not, what can you do to improve that?

3) Explain your feelings about whether your Creator made mistakes in the design of our bodily pleasures.

4) What would you like to change about your connection with your sexual needs, wants, and desires and the messages you have received about bodies and sexuality?

Thoughts and Quotes

Even though I have been raised in a religion and mindset of "one man/one woman" being together forever and I still have it in my own mind that I'd rather have it that way, I feel we are missing the point of what our bodies were fully meant for and what this attraction to another person really means. I wonder what it would be like to live in a society where all people had many partners, without jealousy, and we raised all the children together (like in the Bible)?

~*~

Sex is becoming a huge topic in society today. Different people have a lot of different opinions about sex. Some have positive opinions, and some have bad or negative opinions. For example, the abstinence group that travels around sharing their thoughts on how sex should be hidden until marriage. Today, in recent years these abstinence groups shouldn't even come around because we're getting to the point where we need to be realistic. Now, mostly everyone is having sex. They should have groups coming around talking about sex. Who makes the rules up for people having sex? Who made up a right age for people to have sex? These are questions I have always thought about.

Our attitude toward our body and how we feed and exercise it must match up with Spirit. We came from love, so we must extend that love and appreciation to our body at all times. - Wayne Dwyer

"In our American culture "sensual" is a term used in

conjunction with sexual. The American Heritage Dictionary defines sensual: 'pertaining to or given to the gratification of the physical appetites, especially the sexual appetite. Suggesting lacking in Spiritual or moral interest.' This means if you stop to smell the roses, enjoy watching a rainbow or love the feel of wind on your face, you are immoral." - Dr Susan

"Remind yourself that you are one of the masterpieces that emanated from the universal field of intention. You are unique in the entire history of creation." - Wayne Dwyer

Chapter Five Self-Pleasure

"Noting the placid-withdrawn person as able to accept sensory deprivation and the importance of sensory stimulation to develop healthy individuation and ego formation. It appears there is a correlation between those who are in touch with themselves and others who have learned to be out of touch."
Alexander Lowen, *The Betrayal of the Body*

~*~

The "down there" that is generally our first exploration of the mystery of body sensations begins even before we are born. Boy babies have erections in utero; girl babies lubricate in utero. We are preparing long before birth for our relationship with sensual and sexual exploration. Mothers have asked me what to do with toddlers touching themselves. My answer, "Direct them to a private area where they have permission to explore. Our healthy connection to our genitals is the beginning of our first love affair... as it should be... the You with You. How can you share with others what you like or do not like if you haven't figured it out for yourself? Healthy sexuality begins with healthy self-pleasure, which leads to self-esteem, sexual self-confidence, and loving yourself.

~*~

Masturbation, or self-pleasure, is a very common topic among most teenage boys. They laugh and joke about it, and it is a normal part of a teenage boy's life. We all remember the humorous and embarrassing scenes in TV shows and movies where the viewer "knows" what the young guy is doing. We make light of occurrences like this, but seemingly small events around our sexual development can lead to disconnection and even trauma.

Self-pleasure and masturbation are not usually considered such a normal or common part of a young woman's life. However, women will often self-soothe just by holding their genitals to fall asleep. Pajama parties, back in the day, gave girls the opportunity to express and explore questions or curiosities about their bodies with other females. Today there is much more information available for folks with vulvas to learn techniques for learning and enjoying what they like and do not like, for their own pleasure and orgasmic response. This healthy exploration can lead to communication with a partner for further exploration and understanding of your own pleasure.

Knowing and understanding our sexual selves is certainly very personal and something that many people keep to themselves. It is an activity people may joke about in their teens. That may include picking on other kids or less popular kids, especially in locker rooms or during physical education classes. These negative occurrences can lead to loss of sexual self-esteem or withdrawal from easily communicating about dating and connection with others.

Some common questions that I ask clients to create a history of their self-pleasuring backgrounds include:

- How did you discover masturbation?

- How old were you?

- Did your parent(s) talk with you about it?

- Did your older sibling(s) educate you?

- Were your friends experimenting and sharing?

- Were you ever "caught" masturbating?

- If you were "caught," who "caught" you?

- Was there acceptance or shame?

- Did you discover masturbation by accident?

- Did you use your hand or an object?

- Did you use lotion?

- What did you like to look at while self-pleasuring?

- What did you fantasize about?

- Did you need visual aids?

- Do you still use visual aids?

- Did you feel guilt and shame about self-pleasure when you were young?

- Do you feel guilt and shame about masturbating as an adult?

- If you have a spouse or partner, do they shame or guilt you about this practice of self-love?

- Where did you engage in this time for yourself? The shower? The bathroom? With others?

- Did you rush to finish so you wouldn't get "caught?"

These are some of the questions I discuss during the intake with each new client. Knowing these details about the

person sitting in front of me helps us begin to identify their early sexual wiring. This wiring includes information about how their relationships with themselves began. How they felt about it and if there was guilt and/or shame or if it was a fun and uplifting experience. I want both of us to explore whether there was a dark cloud over them after they connected with themselves in this way. I am curious about those times when they were embarrassed, guilted, or shamed—at home or school, or by friends and neighbors, or while experimenting in the woods or someone's basement—and if it was by people of the same sex, just to give a few examples. This knowledge and these details lead me along a thread to find the behaviors and concerns of the adult, of all the diversities sitting before me.

> *"Greater trauma means greater opportunity for healing."* - Edie Weinstein. "An Independent Study Project: Counseling and Practitioner Views on Utilizing Touch as a Therapeutic Modality"

Details Matter

When I first conduct an intake with a client, we discuss their masturbation routine. It is important that I know details of their self-love behavior. Over time this information will make a difference in how they transfer solo connection to partner connection. When you are young, self-pleasure is often just about "getting off, reaching orgasm." But, like the other growth occurrences we discuss in this book, your mind and body are forming patterns and remembering details and physical sensations from these earliest memories. So what you do and how you do it is important. I do not want you to panic; let me explain.

Examples: When you masturbate, do you use your dry hands or provide lubrication? Do you use a sock or other piece of clothing? Do you lie facedown on the bed or the floor? What are you simulating when you self-pleasure? A picture in a book? A scene from a movie? Do you think about a fantasy, something you saw on the screen or maybe what you heard about other peoples' adventures or experimentation? Ultimately, everyone pretty much agrees that the goal of stimulation is to have the release along with intense sensation called orgasmic response.

Let's get to the nitty-gritty and start with a penis. The idea is to have the shaft surrounded by something warm, moist, and wet. These sensations most replicate the body orifices that are stimulating and arousing. That's why using just a dry hand will take longer and often will hurt over time and "scare" a penis. Masturbating with a dry hand also does not prepare a penis for the times when it will be inside a warm, dark, and wet body when penetrating a partner.

Often my client's first homework assignment is to purchase or order something like the masturbation sleeve. This is a device made of silicone that is used, along with warming gel, to simulate the feel of a partner. The devices that I recommend to my clients are known as male masturbation sleeves. You can find these at http://adameve.com, and my discount code is DOE. By the way, I fire clients who do not do their homework! So when I say your first assignment is to purchase a masturbation device, it is the beginning of the assignments that will lead you down the path of You with You.

For a client with a labia and clitoris, because your anatomy is less prominent, I recommend taking a hand mirror and becoming acquainted with the flower of the folds and the sensitivity that is unique to you. Is your left labia more sensitive than your right labia? (Fun fact - Any of four folds of tissue of the female external genitals are also known as the labium.)

Do you prefer the clitoral hood covering or exposing

these 8,000 nerve endings? Experiment with this, knowing your body supports you in having experiences that you deserve. You can now guide, instruct, and get lost with an informed partner who you have educated about your unique You with You.

Self-pleasure in the shower can work with soap (natural soap with no fragrance, please, for the more sensitive). Lotion or lube is very good in all other situations. There are endless types of lube on the market. Lube comes the closest to simulating the experience of being with a partner.

Also, there is a specific feeling of being "inside" a person, whether it is being inside a vagina, a mouth, or an anus. Each of these has a specific feeling, and each has a different amount of moisture. (Note: Always use plenty of lube, preferably anal lube, for anal sex.) For the most natural and edible option, my favorite lube is coconut oil. It lasts the longest, is nontoxic, and can safely be eaten and inserted.

Now, as you consider the basic details above, do you see why the feeling of masturbating with just your hands or a piece of clothing on your penis is going to feel different than being with a partner, especially when you don't use any lube? If this is how you "get off" for a long time without having partner sex, this is what your body gets used to, and that will create a pattern in your mind and in your bodily response.

When you have sex, and your penis is actually inside a body, and it is feeling so good, warm, and wet with all that moisture, you may find that you reach orgasm much faster than you want. You may also be unable to get an erection or be unable to have an orgasm. This could leave you and your partner frustrated and confused. It is understandable—but it is also easy to explain.

Example: Your body enjoys what you are doing, but this is not what is familiar and not what usually gets you to an orgasmic response. Your body is not used to these sensations, so the mental and physical messages are not there to reach the desired climax that you experience when flying solo. You have literally trained it differently. For a number of my clients that experience this issue, we recommend toys that can simulate being inside a body very well and enhance self-pleasure for all bodies and body parts. (Check out: www.adamevestores.com)

Hurry, Hurry, Hurry

Let's go back to our earlier talk about movies geared toward typical teen comedy. At some point, there is a scene where one of the young guys is rushing through a masturbation opportunity. Or you know what he is doing in his room as his mom is walking down the hall with his clean laundry, and you know she's likely to walk in on him. It is funny in the movies. However, rushing to finish masturbating can become a problem for men. This is another case where your early behaviors are teaching your body a particular pattern and response. Limited time trains your body to hurry and get to the finish line. Whether it is a couple that has limited time or a person masturbating with limited privacy, the body is learning the habit of hurrying up and getting 'er done.

This can and often does lead to premature or delayed

ejaculation in future encounters. This habit can be traced back to having to rush through sexual activity. Remember the time you were on the couch in the recreation room of your girlfriend's parents' house and things had to move quickly! Because of having been focused on getting to the goal, the body doesn't know any other reactions. In our You with You process, we guide clients to work through these early messages to learn how to have a satisfying and fulfilling sex life.

Women and Vibrators

The variety of vibrators and dildos offers many choices in sex toys for women. In group chats or on sex toy reviews, it is not uncommon to see women commenting on how they want stronger and higher speeds. Just a few words about that. Vibrators can certainly be a lot of fun, with a partner and on your own. Also, keep in mind that it is not a good idea to use a vibrator all the time or to continually use it on the highest speed. This can train your body so it will not react as well to human touch, which cannot duplicate the actions created by a machine powered with batteries or electricity. When using vibrators, it is best to vary the routine and the speeds. Remember, vibrators cannot replace the intimacy you can create with your partner. They are fun and serve a purpose, both alone and with others. Variety is the spice of life. Mix it up! Experiment and broaden your experience!

Our Imagination During Self-Pleasuring

What do you imagine or look at during self-pleasuring? There are so many possibilities.

- Porn – online or magazines
- Porn - movies
- Pictures of friends
- Pictures of potential partners
- Pictures of current partner
- Pictures of celebrities
- Pictures of objects

- Pictures of places

In considering "Am I Normal If… " we find what is *natural* for you. What turns you on when you are self-pleasing? What could be the experience of sharing these turn-ons with a partner? Whether alone or with another, build a toolbox of ideas and options for spicing up your me time and your we time. Boredom in the bedroom comes from routine and playing it safe. Stretch! Create! Ask for what you like! Say no thank you to what you don't like! Verbal communication leads to our best physical communication.

You might find interesting, if you enjoy statistics and random tidbits. It's a compilation of information based on data collected in a survey by the Tenga company. There is a lot of interesting information in the report. Click below to view it or download your own copy of the *Tenga 2019 Self-Pleasure Report.* https://www.multivu.com/players/English/8528451-tenga-unveils-2019-self-pleasure-report/docs/Full2019Report_1557144644685-1929663640.pdf

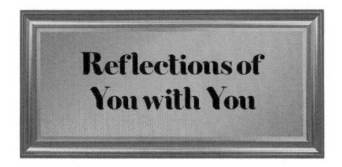

Reflections of You with You

1) Was your first self-pleasure experience scary or pleasant? Why?

2) Were you ever caught enjoying your body, and what sort of reaction did you and anyone else have?

3) Is your relationship with your body one of self-fulfillment and loving connection? Why or why not?

4) Do you walk with shame or guilt related to your masturbation practices? Why do you feel this way?

Thoughts and Quotes

The boys at school would talk and joke about "jerking off," so I figured masturbation was normal behavior for men. I guess the idea I had was that men were supposed to sweep a woman off her feet translated into the belief that a woman did not need to know how to sexually satisfy herself since men were supposed to be able to satisfy her and themselves. This belief was reinforced by the message that women were supposed to be virgins when they married, which came from my parents and religion.

The first person that told me women masturbated, and it was okay for them to, was my mother when I was sixteen. I remember having a conversation with her and my sister. My sister asked her if she had ever masturbated. My mom said she had and that it felt good. That was shocking for me at the time since the only other time someone mentioned the topic was when I was at lunch in high school one day. My friend Allison pointed across the cafeteria to a girl that was not well-liked. She announced to the girls at the table that the girl had admitted to masturbating. The message I got was that girls do not do that and most certainly do not talk about it.

I got very few if any messages about masturbation. The messages I did get were all focused on males masturbating, and in my head, masturbating was something you could only do with a penis. Also, absent from any messages were those relating to arousal in women. I learned all about boys getting erections and having wet dreams, but there was no information, discussion, or explanation of girls being sexually aroused. For a long time when I would be sexually aroused, I thought I had to urinate – and then wondered why I couldn't pee when I went to the bathroom. I don't even remember thinking that I could give myself an orgasm until I was almost out of high school, which is when I first remember masturbating with the intention of reaching orgasm. After that, I thought it was the best thing I had ever discovered. Even then I never talked about it, and the fact that I hadn't had sex prevented me from talking with any of my peers about myself in a sexual way.

~*~

Sexuality for me was a taboo until my thirteenth birthday, when I started to experience feelings with my whole body. I started to see some changes everywhere, and it was hard to understand why that was happening and, worse, why I was starting to forget thinking about playing with Barbies and caring more about the way I looked and how I started to feel when boys were near me!

~*~

I started masturbating at age thirteen. My parents were very emotionally abusive, so I retreated to my room a lot and masturbated at least six times a day until around age forty-eight. I used porn instead of having relationships, and this finally prompted me to seek help.

~*~

I was about twelve when I started to self-pleasure. It was joked about at school, and I felt guilty at first. That didn't stop me, but it didn't help either.

~*~

Started self-pleasure around ten years old. I would look at German lingerie catalogs. The women have very beautiful, natural bodies. They were not like the bodies you see now on porn with the fake skinny bodies. But even with this, I was unable to get an erection.

~*~

Masturbation is a meditation on self-love. So many of us are afflicted with self-loathing, bad body image, shame about our bodily functions, and confusion about sex and pleasure. I recommend an intense love affair with yourself. - Betty Dodson, The Grandmother of Masturbation

~*~

The only shame in masturbation is the shame of not doing it well. - Sigmund Freud

~*~

"If we don't own our own orgasms, we don't own our own bodies; we don't own our own lives."

 - Betty Dodson, The Grandmother of Masturbation

Thirds Theory

of

Self-Actualization

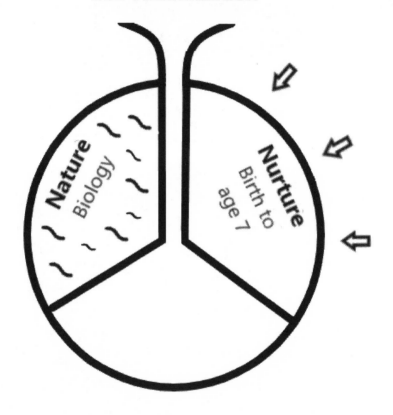

Chapter Six You with Others

"It appears that if we do not develop as tactile beings, we become insensitive to the needs of others."

- Susan Kaye, Master's Thesis: *Sensory Deprivation Effects on Personality* 1998

You cannot give away something you do not have for yourself. Your relationship journey begins with You with You. Building your self-esteem and sexual self-confidence is the foundation that is then translated to your connection with others. The You with You toolbox we are building together, with both verbal and physical communication, is the handbook that you share with a potential partner. Verbal communication paves the way to physical communication. We are building the bridge of trust and possibly relating experiences that can bring short-term joy or a lifetime commitment.

"Social and sexual education is a very important

aspect of surrogate treatment. The sensate focus socialization skills are designed to teach the client social skills and sexual information they need to attain social and sexual ability. Most clients feel they need instructions on how to conduct themselves in social settings. They also admit they need their sexual questions answered to distinguish between sexual myths and misinformation from fact." - Susan Kaye, Dissertation

~*~

Up to this point in the book, our focus has been on your background and identifying your early relationship messages. We use this information during sessions to guide us in identifying possible issues in existing and potential relationships. This is where the rubber meets the road as you move forward into the You with Others phase. Knowing the early messages that do not serve you gives you a heads-up on how to avoid future problems.

You with Others includes your early relationships with others or having had limited experience with others.

Did that affect your social growth and development? Some children had to come straight home from school to do chores, particularly if they lived in a rural area. Some kids could not participate in after-school activities, perhaps because their parents worked and they had to come straight home from school.

These situations can deprive children of social opportunities and give them limited time to be with other children or people outside their immediate family. This can make it difficult to develop adequate social skills, less communicative, and they may be shy, and more introverted. These traits carry into adulthood for many children and make it difficult to not feel socially awkward.

Here are a few examples of young children having had limited socialization skills practice:

- In first grade you say to the little girl in front of you that she's cute, and she replies, "Oh you're disgusting." Later in life, a woman turns you down for a date and, in your mind, all women still think you're disgusting.

- In fourth grade you ask a girl to a dance, and she says no. Later in life, you remember that rejection and have problems approaching women to ask them on dates.

These scenarios paint pictures that are not about you. Most are projections of the other person's insecurities, fears, and their early messages, which formulate behaviors in them. This traces back to their early rejections and childhood messages. I do not look to clean up what happened. I want to know how we got here, what we have to work with, where we go from here, and *how we move you forward*.

On the other hand, some children in these situations may go totally in the opposite direction because they are seeking attention. They may reach out to inappropriate partners, or an excessive number of partners, as substitute "father figures" or "mother figures." Some may dress in provocative ways because they find additional attention—even if it is unhealthy and unsafe, attention. These behaviors can easily carry over into adulthood without their realizing when, how, and why their actions began.

Children are raised in varying scenarios. Some are raised by grandparents or family members because their parents are gone, or other relatives are their caregivers while their parents work. These scenarios can have different effects on the child depending on the caregiver's feelings about their involvement. Sadly, there are situations where parents have abandoned their children and responsibilities, making everyone's lives more difficult.

I have also seen cases where children were better off with another relative while a biological parent worked on their personal issues. Parents who are unable to sustain a healthy, loving relationship with their child pass on disconnect and social inhibitions. No matter the reason *why* a child is in any situation, it will have an impact on them throughout their life.

We have talked before about the fact that children need love, touch, and nurturing, especially when they are young. In some of these situations, they do not get the love, touch, and nurturing we all need. When a client begins their inner work, we consider the people they grew up around. This could include the people who raised them, relatives, siblings, friends that visited, and others. It might also include an alcoholic parent, a parent with a physical or mental health issue, and/or parents who worked long hours. Maybe it included a relative or family friend who was mentally, physically, or emotionally abusive, a coach or someone in the church who touched them in a way that did not feel right, and on and on.

There are many examples I could cite of You with Others that impact relationships later in life. You may not think about these connections or realize there is any correlation as an adult, but these experiences from birth to age five set the stage for your adult life. As I listen to stories and ask what I call... the right question at the right time, I can see the thread of You with You from birth to the you that is sitting with me.

That is why you and I are here—together!

~*~

"These early years are a time in life when a child is especially vulnerable and when traumas can happen to them. The child may not consciously remember

details of events for many years, but those memories are buried and will usually manifest for them in some way." Dr. Carol Cobb Nettleton

Throughout the years, I have heard about a wide variety of instances, including:

- A child was left behind by their parents and they were kept in a basement.

- A child was locked in a closet when parents were home.

- Mother said, "Wait till your father gets home," and that meant he would beat them.

- A first-time mother was nervous and scared to hold her newborn baby, and the baby could sense that. They still have trauma, as an adult, when they are touched.

Each of the examples above can have a variety of effects on us. The work we do together is to figure out what happened and what are the first steps to take toward healing. Do we need deeper neck up work, such as EMDR (see description below) or another specialized therapist? Or do we begin with hands-on bodywork, such as cuddling or movement therapy? We work together, in this team approach, to wrap clients up in a mind-body wellness commitment to support you and resolve it. This is why, over the years, I've handpicked a team of specially qualified practitioners. I have personally trained many of the people I work with to help my clients. I am on the lookout for new people and new modalities all the time, to expand the possibilities to help our clients.

EMDR (Eye Movement Desensitization and Reprocessing)

Whether we've experienced small setbacks or major traumas, we are all influenced by memories and experiences we may not remember or don't fully understand. Life events *can harbor themselves in our bodies, trauma or drama stuck in our cellular memories. These memories become trapped into feelings causing us to hold beliefs and act in ways that do not serve us. EMDR is a brain science that through the use of rapid eye movements can break apart unconscious and automatic reactions, thoughts and behaviors. "Don't let yourself be run by unconscious and automatic reactions."* Francine Shapiro, PhD Creator of EMDR *Getting Past your Past*

I had a client whose older brothers and sisters moved out, and he was the only child at home. His father left when his mother got sick. So, he had to come straight home from school to care for his mother. As an adult, he ended up with a woman he was going to take care of, like his mother. He avoided any actual romantic relationship with this woman without realizing the correlation to the relationship he had with his mother.

This situation was his "normal" since that was how he had grown up. This pattern had been wired into his cellular memory and just "felt right" to him. Most if not all, of my clients need bodywork. There are triggers within the cellular memory of the body.

I shared an example of cellular memory in Chapter 2: the woman who, during our session, discovered the memory of being hung, with her arms stretched over her head, in a barn when she was a child. That is just one example of how this can work that I've seen over the years. There have been many, many others. Specialized bodywork is the core of this very specialized therapy process.

Reflections of You with Others

1) Do you feel your early years set you up or let you down for connection and relationships with others? Why do you feel this way?

2) Are your cellular memories generating wanted and healthy relationships? Do you have thoughts about why or why not?

3) Did you develop adequate social skills to be able to share yourself easily in a group setting? What do you feel contributed or what holds you back?

4) Is lack of self-confidence or even self-love keeping you from living a life you would love? Why do you feel this way?

Thoughts & Quotes

"Those who are comfortable with touch were more talkative, cheerful, socially dominant, non-conforming, less afraid and suspicious of other people's motives and intentions and have less anxiety and tension in their everyday lives. People who are less comfortable with touch tend to be more emotionally unstable, socially withdrawn, and more apprehensive about communicating and had lower self-esteem." Montagu, Schultz, and Zubek

~*~

"You probably grew up in a family and community that did not know how to nurture your innate sexual curiosity and play. No one gave you a model for cultivating great sex, instead, you may have encountered silence, shame and mixed messages. Isn't it time you take the lead and plan a pleasurable path for your precious partnerships?"

Charla Hathaway, Eight Erotic Nights

Chapter Seven Relationship Firsts

"Instant chemistry feels great! It is raw, organic emotion. The art and science of relationship chemistry is still a mystery to me, but it is always a delight when it happens. You certainly know when you feel it, and that sizzle begins many a new relationship."

— Susan C. Young, *The Art of Body Language: 8 Ways to Optimize Non-Verbal Communication for Positive Impact*

~*~

Nearly everyone that completes my initial intake process knows the name of the person that was their first attraction, the color of that person's hair, and the factor that made them remember this person for twenty, thirty, or even fifty years. Something in us is touched so powerfully, and it is unusual and long-lasting when that delight happens. The first kiss, first hand holding, and first love never leave us. They are part of the jigsaw puzzle that is called "you." The puzzle pieces create powerful feelings, which we seek and long to re-create in those first and life-changing experiences.

~*~

Few things in life are as memorable as and will affect us like our first attractions. At any phase of our lives, we seem to remember our first crush, the first time our hand brushed against that cute boy or girl in class or on the playground—accidentally of course. We remember that first awkward kiss or the first time we reached for their hand, whether it was hesitantly under the table or boldly in front of everyone.

Whether we want to or not, we also remember that first rejection, or multiple rejections. When you got the nerve to ask him or her to a dance or out for a soda and they said no—or, worse, they may have laughed at you.

Our relationships with others affect us on many levels, and on levels that we are not always consciously aware of. That is why this is often so important in my work. There are many elements of these relationships that we do remember, but there are other elements that are remembered in our bodies, on a cellular level, that can and do impact our relationships. We have to dig to find and to resolve those to improve our relationships. This is what I call a "thread" that runs all through our lives, to our very core. It includes physical and mental memories, and it can disconnect us from our bodies. I will share examples of how that works, throughout the chapter, to help you understand.

First Attraction

That first person you were attracted to—what made them stand out? Why were they so different? We may not remember, but there was just something about them. The "thing" that made them attract our attention was likely heavily affected by the age we were at the time. Whether we remember what attracted us, it is very likely we remember the person, right down to the smallest details. Many of us still know them. Remember those feelings—there

was something different about that person.

- Maybe they were at the top of the slide on the playground and the sun was shining in their blonde hair.

- Or maybe they were playing on the Little League team.

- Maybe she had her hair in ponytails and looked gorgeous in her new school outfit, and all the boys wanted to carry her books to class.

- It could be that she was starting to develop and that sweater made her chest look bigger than it was, and none of the boys could stop staring.

- The boy next door had been your best friend since second grade; now he had just been named the captain of the football team and you just noticed him in a different way, in his uniform. Had he always been that cute and had that great body?

- She had the dorm room across the hall from yours and her great laugh carried across the hall. You wondered if her voice and face were great too. It would be nice of you to offer to help her move in.

First, we identify your first attraction. Who was this person, a girl or a boy? How old were you at the time? Where did you meet them? These details can make a difference. If you were very young, it was likely at school, church, in your neighborhood, or with friends. When you're older, you can meet at college, at work, online on social media or in chatrooms, or just about anywhere in public.

First Hand-Holding or Touch

How many times have you "accidentally" brushed up against someone in line? It seems like it was easier when we were younger and in school, especially on the playground or in class. Maybe in a rush at the end of the school period, when we were putting things away. That cute girl with red hair and freckles was beside you, and you touched her arm when you reached to put something on the shelf. Or you had been too shy to talk to the new boy that moved into your second-grade class, but when the teacher wanted someone to hand out the graded tests, you volunteered. It was a great excuse to say hi to him and ask his name, and he might even touch your hand.

These things may sound silly to us as adults but remember when you were seven or eight and had that first crush. We did various things to find a way to touch the person who caught our attention. We found a way to brush up against them or accidentally bump into them.

As we get older, we may introduce ourselves and shake their hand, and wait a little too long to let go. Sometimes we may walk up and hug someone and hug them too long or too close. Have you sat with a person and found yourself touching their hand or arm as you talk to them? Was that because you were interested in them, and did you feel a rush of excitement?

First Contact

Often the first touch and first contact go hand in hand.

After that special person caught your eye and you knew you were interested, what did you do? It can be really difficult to get up the nerve to make the first move. This chapter is all about those relationship "firsts," and a first move is definitely a big deal for most people.

We have an impulse and desire to jump in and say something or do something, but maybe the hands are sweaty; the armpits may be sweaty. Young guys might be stumbling over their feet and "falling" over their words. Isn't it amazing how many ways your arms, legs, mouth, and mind can all let you down at the same time? We've all had the same thing happen to us, and it is so frustrating.

Even worse is when a person has caught your attention, and you are trying to get the nerve to go up to them for the first time or to tell them you are interested in them, and someone else gets to them first. It might be a friend, or maybe it is someone who is able to talk to girls or guys much more easily than you can. Do they have brothers or sisters and just seem to be more comfortable around groups? Or you may not understand why others can talk to people so much more easily than you can.

You do know that it is very irritating, and you need to find a way to break through the fog and confusion that stops you from being able to talk to that beautiful girl you want to sit with on the subway. Or is it the guy with the dark eyes that goes to the same coffee shop you visit at lunch?

Let's take an example of a young boy in school who likes a girl, and he goes up to her on the playground. Which of these things happens, and how does he react? Each of these things will have a different effect on him as a child, and it will make a difference as he gets older and is dating too.

- Is he confident when he approaches her?
- Does he stutter or stammer when he walks up to her?

- Does he look her in the eye and talk or look down at the ground?

- Is she nice to him?

- Does she laugh at him and insult him?

- Does she say he has cooties or some similar comment?

- Does he ask her to a dance or to do something else with him?

- If he does ask her something, does she say yes or no?

- Is she nice or mean in her reply?

- If she says yes, does she try to kiss him?

- If she says no, does she try to hit him?

- How does he react?

- Does she go tell her friends about it, and is what she says good or bad?

First Rejection

It takes a lot of nerve for us to let someone know that we like them. We can do that by saying we like them. Or we can ask them to do something with us, maybe go to a dance, to a movie or to get something to eat.

All these situations make us vulnerable, and for most people, at any age, it is hard to put ourselves into a position where we are vulnerable. We are giving that person the chance to hurt us or to embarrass us. Either of those options can have a lasting effect on us, especially when we are young.

It does not have to be harmful to us, but for some people, it can be. For example, how would you react to this situation? Consider this happening to you in elementary school then happening to you as an adult. Let's say there is a person you think is wonderful, and you're both on the playground. There is a special event, and you need a partner. You want to ask this person to be your partner for the day, and you've gotten up your nerve to ask them. You walk over to them and ask if they would go to the event with you. They look at you and suddenly laugh out loud.

As we grow older, these earlier experiences come to mind the next time we want to invite someone to dinner or for a drink. Their laughter or rejection or maybe a mean comment may come to mind. Sometimes we can brush it off and ask them anyway.

Other times we may not be able to ask them without feeling hesitant or embarrassed. Sometimes, that hesitation makes us decide not to reach out to them at all. Or it makes us resist the temptation to ask out the people we really want to date. Instead, we may settle for people who don't intimidate us or embarrass us. This can be overcome, but first, we have to understand how the problem started in order to fix it.

First Kiss

Ahh, the first kiss. Is there anything like that first kiss? We see so many movie scenes and candid pictures of young children and first kisses. What about your first kiss? I'm not talking about your aunt or uncle. This is the first kiss with someone that you were attracted to. Someone that gave you butterflies in your stomach. Maybe it was someone in school that sat near you. Maybe someone on the playground, at summer camp, or even from church, and you snuck a kiss.

Did you fumble and maybe even miss their mouth the

first time? Was it wet and slobbery, or was your mouth dry because you were nervous? Sometimes, it is an attempt to move an arm around the girl and then kiss her and totally missing your aim. But, eventually, the lips lock, and even if the technique needs work, for a moment, it is wonderful.

It is interesting, even when the first time is not great, we do not seem to remember that. The other person may have a memory of things that were done wrong, but we can remember it was great. And it is hard to forget who we shared that first kiss with. If I asked you, I bet you could tell me who it was, where you were, and how it went. So tell me, are you smiling?

First Intercourse

The first time we have sex is something that will have a lasting effect on us. How it will affect you depends on a number of things. These include how you have been raised to view sex, your early messages about sex, the details of your first experience, your religious views about sex, the messages you get about sex from your family, peers, and religion after you have sex, and many other things.

These are some of the factors that will impact your experience –

- Did you have sex with someone you cared about?

- Were you forced to have sex?

- Did you consent to have sex?

- Were drugs or alcohol involved?

- Was it a one-night stand?

- Was it with someone that you knew and were in a relationship with?

- Was it planned or spontaneous?

- Was it painful or comfortable?

- Did you and/or your partner have any idea what you were doing?

- Were you and/or your partner virgins?

- How old were you?

- Where were you?

- Was your first time a sexual assault?

- The first time you had sex, did you get

pregnant?

The answers to many of these questions can start you on the path to sexual dysfunction. They can also begin difficulties in life depending on your age and situation.

1) Can you name that first person who caught your eye in grade school that had you feel something you knew was different? What was different about them?

2) Where and who was your first kiss? Are you still in communication or even friends today? What made this kiss so memorable?

3) Was your first intercourse a positive or negative experience, and did it have a long-lasting or permanent effect? How would you explain it?

4) How would you advise a young person entering this world of "firsts"?

Thoughts & Quotes

My first memory of a girl was when I was in the first grade. Her name was Nicole and she was in the fifth grade. She was a little cutie and the most popular girl in the school. I remember I wrote down on a piece of paper, I Love Nicole. I had this piece of paper in my desk drawer at home. One day, my mom and I were cleaning my room and she found it. She showed it to my dad right away. He knew this girl and her family. He knows everyone, being a teacher! Then the next day in school, he called me out into the hallway in the middle of class and then had her come into the hallway and told her about my note. I was so embarrassed, and I think I almost cried! From that point on, I was scared to tell my parents anything that had to do with girls. I was afraid of girls because I didn't want to feel that way again.

~*~

There was just kissing and fondling that took place

until I was about twenty-one, when I finally gave it up to a guy I really liked. But it was more like I just needed to get rid of my virginity, so it might as well be with someone I really liked and I knew would be as gentle as he could. He fell asleep and there I was wondering what was the big deal—kind of a non-event. I did not really feel much pleasure in this further act. This did not lead to any relationship with this guy, and I didn't have sex again for a while.

Then there was the man who was the first to give me the oral sex I wasn't sure I was ready for, but since no one else had offered, I just did it. An odd experience, but I felt very cared for and taken care of by this honest man, who not only amazed and delighted me with many new sexual experiences but allowed love to enter my life. We had three great months together, then he went back to school and I went on to other experiences. The other thing he showed me was how selfish my previous lovers had been, and I was beginning to see that there was more to sex than just sex.

Our first time together was not really good at all. He was gentle and very careful, but it was extremely painful. It was kind of funny since I screamed and started yelling at him, but he just hugged me and told me to relax and enjoy it. He said it was going to be better and that everything was going to be fine but that never happened and I was so stressed and nervous, so he finally took it out and I started to cry. He went to take a shower and I decided to join him. I felt that he deserved me more than anyone else. I got in the shower and we started having sex again. Even if it was painful, I pretended that everything was OK and that I was enjoying it.

When I was in the seventh grade, I was twelve years old. This is when I had my first sexual encounter. This girl was in the ninth grade, and she was in love with me. She gave me oral sex at a playground across the street from my house. I remember all of my friends used to say how they did it and how great it felt. So I had to try it. I was talking to this girl for about three weeks. We used to walk from school and to the YMCA together.

One day on the way back from the YMCA, we stopped at the playground near my house, and we started doing little flirty things. One thing led to another, and she started to unzip my pants. At this point, my heart was pounding. I was so nervous it wasn't funny and it was noticeable. I started to blush and to get jumpy. I was like that because she was older and she intimidated me. She said, "Chill out, I'm not going to hurt you, just relax."

She proceeded to give me oral sex. She only did it for about two minutes and I ejaculated. It was the biggest sensation that I'd felt in my life. After that, we simply went home. That whole night I was thinking about it. I didn't know what she would say to everyone, but I didn't really sweat it. This was kind of an icebreaker. After that, I wasn't hesitant to let girls perform oral sex on me.

~*~

In my early forties I'm still nervous to ask a woman on a date. Friends say I'm a good-looking guy, and I've been married twice, but after a recent divorce, I'm shy about asking a woman out. Thinking back, I remember a really cute girl on a playground in third grade that I asked to a school dance. I really liked her, and I finally got the nerve to ask her out. I walked right up to her and asked her to the dance, and she laughed in my face. Right there on the playground in front of everyone. Every time I think about asking someone out, I think of her laughing in my face. Even all these years later.

Chapter Eight Socialization is a Core Focus

"For some men, the problem is that they are very shy and find it extremely difficult to meet women or to ask them out" - Zilbergeld, 1999.

In writing my dissertation, a number of themes emerged based on face-to-face interviews and case notes from 151 clients. These notes were taken from the records of three professional surrogate coaches. The clients' responses were recorded during their history-taking process. In exploring their social concerns, several themes became evident. The largest themes included lack of social/sexual confidence, inexperience, shyness, and anxiety around social situations. The outcomes the surrogates wanted for these clients was to feel comfortable in their own skin when interacting with a partner or when attempting to interact in social situations. The dissertation data identified social and sexual barriers that prevented each client from being able to experience healthy relationships and the feeling of sexual well-being.

In this chapter, I will share details about the tools and the sensate focus exercises that were used with the participants. These study participants were also given socially interactive homework assignments including both practice with a surrogate partner and finding dating partners on their own.

Because of the sensate focus and socialization skills homework, 68 percent of the participants were able to leave the Surrogate Partner Program before entering the sexual education component. Normally, Surrogate Partner Therapy would include sexual education, but these clients had already made significant progress in their areas concern. This data proved my hypothesis regarding the importance of the social skills trainings and the sensate focus exercises. It really is a core part of our work!

"Sexologists around the world continue to utilize

Sensate Focus structured touching exercises which are the foundations of sex therapy." (Albaugh & Kellogg-Spadt, 2002)

In the 1960s, Masters and Johnson created what they called sensate focus exercises. This 12-step program is used to mainly reduce anxiety while learning what feels good and what does not, through non-demanding, structured and timed touch exercises. You are taken on a therapeutic journey of these timeless exercises which are still the core of sex therapy today. Through the books written on sensate focus you will learn about the hand caress, the head caress, mirror work, front body and back body just to name a few. –

The step-by-step guidebook: *Touching for Pleasure*

by Adele Kennedy, Surrogate Partner and Susan Dean, Ph.D.,

Getting to the core of what stops us from putting ourselves into social situations and engaging in social interaction is critical to healing the You with You, which then more easily flows into You with Others. In Dr. Tova Feder's book *Sex Is the Least of It*, she addresses a very important point. Throughout the pages, she explains that it is our ability to first connect with our own needs, wants, and desires—our own sensuality—sharing ourselves mentally, physically, and emotionally, that is paramount to "reach out and touch" someone with a healthy level of comfort. This allows a person to move from the safety of the self and reach out confidently and securely to connect, and bond, with potential dating partners and life partners.

At this time, little research had been done about surrogate treatment. Based on my academic research and my clinical work, I knew it could help clients alleviate social and sexual problems and remedy diagnosed disorders. During my research we identified social and sexual issues that held clients back from experiencing healthy relationships and the feeling of sexual well-being.

To help the client overcome these issues, the

treatment combines social and sexual therapeutic modalities or exercises. An important part of the treatment is called the triadic model. This includes the working relationship between the surrogate, the client, and the therapist—working as a triad in the treatment of the client.

I studied the records of three professional surrogate coaches. These records included 151 single Caucasian males who primarily resided in the eastern United States and were treated in a surrogate coaching program between 1977 and 1992.

My purpose with this study was to accomplish two main things:

1) To determine the degree of success that could be achieved in correcting the clients' problems
2) To achieve the clinical resolution of their diagnosed social and/or sexual disorders

In the research we found some similarities and several themes the clients had in common, based on the surrogate coaches' interviews with them and the details they recorded in their files. These themes are very familiar to many of us in our dating lives and our relationships.

These themes include such familiar topics as: 1) fear of women, 2) lack of social and sexual confidence and experience, 3) shyness and anxiety in social and sexual situations, 4) inability to develop and maintain intimate relationships, 5) lack of social and sexual education, 6) inability to perform sexually, 7) emotional and mental pain from childhood abuse, and 8) lack of sexual desire.

The reasons for some of these issues could come from many different sources. It could be socioeconomic, influenced by education at home or school, dependent on their age, based on their religious background, and based on their masturbation history and/or practices, to name a few. Through my research I found that clients who participated in and completed the sensate focus exercises were able to resolve their diagnosed disorders.

Several variables were studied, including age;

socioeconomic, educational, and religious backgrounds; and masturbation practices. None of these factors limited the success of the sensate focus socialization techniques in surrogate treatment. I realize this could appear very narrow and biased due to the 151 participants being Caucasian males from the East Coast. However, since this dissertation, I have worked with many clients of different genders, ages, geographical locations, different races, socioeconomic levels, educational backgrounds, and much more. The fact is that these tools and techniques apply to EVERYONE. They are tools for humanity. Tools that offer an ability for deep connection through touch and talk—our most basic ingredients for connection with self and others.

The information gathered from their interviews and the recordings of the surrogates' experiences with each client provides insight into and more deeply evaluates the surrogate treatment program. The interviews are reported by the surrogates in a narrative style, which includes the surrogates' feelings and observations of each client's experience.

Client Story - #1

One client, B, expresses fear of women, particularly female genitalia. B's diagnosed problem is late-life virginity. He has carried through his life the scars of emotional abuse inflicted by his mother. B came to surrogate treatment because he could "see the years slipping away from him and his dream to have a wife and family was feeling further and further from his reach."

B's surrogate coach, C, discloses the background details which led him into treatment. B is a forty-three-year-old Catholic attorney who describes his problem as "virginity, extreme fear, and anxiety around women and sex." His stated goal is "to have intercourse, feel comfortable with female genitalia."

B started masturbating at fourteen years of age with, as he says, "a lot of guilt and shame." His masturbation practices when he began therapy were "infrequent." Also at age fourteen, his mother began telling him stories about how horrible and painful sex is for women. She told him stories of her visits to the gynecologist and that she needed a drink, a whiskey sour, when she got home from one of these appointments. She also told him that sex was causing her permanent harm and she wanted her doctor to verify that fact so she could justify not having any more sex.

B's first sexual experience was during his college years. He was in a relationship with a girl he cared for very much. They had been dating for quite some time, and the petting sessions were "heating up." He said that he was "very nervous and scared," but during one of these "heated dates," he reached down and touched her genitalia. Her response to his touch was "ouch, that hurt." From this point on, B has been afraid to go far enough with women to "hurt them."

B had been in talk therapy for five years when he entered the surrogate treatment program. His talk therapist told him about the surrogate process. B met with his surrogate over the phone a few times before he agreed to proceed with treatment. B and the surrogate met at a mutually agreed upon hotel for a three-day weekend intensive. He was successful in performing the sensate focus techniques and was able to engage in oral sex and intercourse. He and his therapist were very pleased at his ability to accomplish so much in this short period of time.

Conclusion

My statistical analysis showed that teaching our clients sensate focus exercises and socialization skills was effective regardless of their religion, occupation, living arrangements, and masturbation practices. Most subjects were successful in completing the sensate focus techniques, at an 82 percent rate.

In this study, 68 percent of 151 subjects, pulled from the files of three female surrogate partners, completed the sensate focus exercises and resolve their concerns. Today, through our Integrative Mind-Body Therapies institute, we have trained surrogate partners who work with all diversities, including clients who are cisgender male, gay, lesbian, transgender, nonbinary, and of all sizes, ages, shapes, and ethnicities.

Emergent Themes

The emergent themes that became clearly evident are:

1) Fear of Women

2) Lack of Social/Sexual Confidence and Experience

3) Shyness and Anxieties Around Social and Sexual Situations

4) Inability to Develop Intimate Relationships

5) Need for Social/Sexual Education

6) Freedom From Emotional and Mental Pain of Childhood Abuse

7) Lack of Desire

8) Fear About the Need to Perform

These themes or patterns fit into nine categories, which include:

1) Social Phobia

2) Late-life Virginity

3) Erectile Dysfunction

4) Premature Ejaculation

5) Sexual Orientation

6) Mental and/or Physical Disabilities

7) Avoidant Personality

8) Orgasmic Disorder

9) Aversion Disorders

Social and Sexual Education

Social and sexual education is a very important aspect of surrogate treatment. The sensate focus socialization skills are designed to teach the client social skills and sexual information he needs to improve his social and sexual ability. Twenty-six of the subjects said they needed instructions on how to conduct themselves in social settings, particularly with women. They also admitted that they needed their sexual questions answered to recognize sexual myths and to sort misinformation from fact.

A group of people that need social and sexual education is the mentally and physically challenged. In this research, six out of the nine physically challenged clients stated their need for this training. Some of the acceptable sex therapy strategies in rehabilitation centers for the head injured include: 1. Education about basic anatomy and physiology, pregnancy, contraceptives, and sexually transmitted diseases; 2. Social skills training focused on dating skills; 3. Counseling to encourage emotional expression; and 4. Community social experiences that have a high probability of success.

These guidelines do not incorporate any hands-on sex help. There is a need for sexuality training that is not being addressed. I am referring to the people who could enjoy and benefit from sexual activities and are not able to obtain this type of training. There are many physical, mental, and emotional benefits to sex and the intimacy that can go along with sex. All humans can and should have the opportunity to experience these benefits in their lives. Surrogate treatment offers the hands-on sexual training that the physically challenged are unable to procure from basic clinical services.

Client Story #2 - Social and Sexual Education

N is a physically challenged client who uses a wheelchair. This client's mother contacted a therapist because her son was constantly having erections and he was also inappropriate with women in public. N stated in his interview with the surrogate that he "wanted to learn more about his potential for sex and sensuality." N was twenty-five years of age when he started surrogate treatment. He had been disabled in a car accident when he was a teenager. His mother contacted a sex therapist because she felt that N should have social and sexual training.

I first met N when I went out to speak with his parents. It was discovered that N had spent a lot of time in the hospital where I was employed as a nurse. The surrogate stated that when she agreed to work with their son, the parents hugged her and, with tears in their eyes, said, "Thank God for good people like you." In the first session, it was clear that N had very limited knowledge of his body and that he needed to learn where his sensitive areas were located. N is a quadriplegic, but he had limited use of his hands. "We did the head caress, and it was hard for him to give to me because of his physical limitations, but he did have a lovely touch." We found that N was able to use the sensuality tools. He enjoyed the discovery of different sensations from the feathers, massage oil, and fur mitt.

Because we would not be incorporating the socialization homework, by session three we were exploring genital pleasuring. We were able to find a technique for N to masturbate to orgasm. He was very excited about this, and so were his parents. In session five N wanted me to get dressed up in sexy clothing. I wore garters and high heels, and his mother thought this was great. I tried to educate N to go more slowly and not grab at me when I walked in the door. I wanted him to show respect to me, learn to be respectful of other women, and consider their feelings. We practiced role playing appropriate behavior when in the presence of a woman, particularly one that he finds attractive.

I asked about the possibilities of N finding a partner or even an appropriate love interest. The surrogate replied, "Social isolation is a major problem for this population. I have experienced many disabled clients who suffer from isolation, loneliness, and a longing for both social and sexual contact. So much of the outside world is closed off to them. This is one of the reasons that surrogate treatment is an important service for this special population. Together we can explore their bodies and find their sensitive, erotic zones. If they can learn how to pleasure themselves, they then at least can obtain some relief and possible release from their sexual frustration."

The surrogate continues with her narrative: "I saw N once a month for two years. He suffered from depression because of his situation, and sometimes our sessions were not pleasant. He would cry a lot from the frustration of wanting a girlfriend. He would get crushes on women he would see at the mall when he and his parents went shopping and would become even more depressed because he was unnoticed by the women."

Our sessions ended when N and his family moved to Florida. They made this move for N's health and so he would be able to venture outdoors all through the year and not be even more isolated during the winter season. At this writing, the surrogate is still in contact with N and his parents. They often send Christmas cards and family pictures. The parents have shared with her that the sessions helped their son. "[We are] grateful for your blend of love and professionalism."

Case Conclusion

Through the process of the sensate focus exercises, many clients in this study were able to overcome, in varying degrees, their concerns and problems that inhibited their sexual lives. With the help and guidance of their surrogate coach, they gained trustworthy, reliable, factual, and truthful social and sexual education.

The virgins were able to face their fears and embarrassment over being with women who were more sexually experienced than themselves. All clients were given the opportunity to explore a woman's body, ask questions, and be vulnerable. In a safe environment, provided by their surrogate coach, they could practice the physical capabilities of their own bodies. They learned to focus more on what they could do, sexually, and to focus less on what they could not do sexually. Gaining confidence and experience allowed them to overcome fears of not being able to perform sexually.

The surrogate coach, using the sensate focus socialization skills, taught these clients how to dance, how to take a woman out on a date, how to be appropriate in social settings such as a restaurant, cocktail party, or singles club. They learned how to make that first phone call and ask for a date and then how to create a romantic setting using candles, soft music, fragrances, and intimate conversation.

Surrogate coaching opened social and sexual doors for these clients, which provided, for most of them, a freedom and happiness that they had possibly never known before. They gained experience and were given the opportunity to further their potential to obtain their life goals that had been inhibited by social and sexual fears and problems.

The completion of the sensate focus socialization

process has given them training that is not available to clients in any other field of treatment. The integration of professional physical, hands-on sex work and reputable talk therapy is unique to the surrogate treatment process.

> The final results of this study showed that 86 percent of the clients completed the socialization process, and 62 percent completed the entire treatment and resolved their diagnosed problems. This supports my conclusion that surrogate coaching is a valuable treatment process that combines social therapeutic modalities with sexual therapeutic modalities to provide a very unique experience for those persons who seek resolution of both perceived and real social and sexual limits and problems.

Note: The idea of surrogate treatment for this population raises two issues. One concern is the legal, moral, and ethical use of surrogate coaches.

The second issue is whether physically challenged people should be sexual. For many physically challenged people, family and/or caretakers do not want to deal with the sexual needs or desires of someone they feel should be asexual. N was fortunate that his family was willing to acknowledge that he had sexual needs and frustrations and that they agreed to acquire the services of a surrogate coach for him.

Today we include all mind-body touch and talk modalities. This study was conducted on males without primary partners to practice sexual and social skills. The most important part of the treatment, at its core, are the exercises known throughout the sex therapy community as sensate focus exercises. These practices were initially designed for sex therapy with couples by the sex researchers Masters & Johnson. These core practices were created and are still taught to and utilized by anyone in the sexual field. Sensate focus exercises are necessary for diagnosis of sexual dysfunction, and for anyone who is practicing these exercises and skills, it will help them to reach certain sexual and/or social goals.

Janet Shares Thoughts as a Surrogate Partner

Surrogate partner therapy centers on the whole person and their experience, first with themselves and then with others. For much of the beginning of the work, we work on, in Susan's words, "You with You," which begins with introducing or recreating their personal relationship with themselves. Once we have made that relationship more solid, we can begin the work of socialization. Then we can transition to "You with Others." The work is specialized to their specific needs and areas of growth.

Socialization can begin with their ability to receive feedback on how I experience them. Their presence has an impact on me, and I can openly share what that is like. For some clients, no one has ever shared with them what it is like to be in a relationship with them or to be near them.

This feedback includes everything from the way they

dress to what they smell like. I have an experience that is limited to just being mine. It is valuable for them to know others may have similar experiences with them or many other things that are completely unknown to them. Our clients can walk around in the world without knowing how other people experience them, and it's worth considering what that might be about and opening their curiosity about how others perceive them.

We begin here.

From there, we consider how they communicate. In the beginning of the work, we focus on their own style of communication. With time, we begin to weave into our sessions opportunities to listen with reflective listening or completion loops. Listening is a special skill that requires practice and can be fatiguing if they haven't practiced the slower pace of reflecting back what they heard from me. In an age where we run to get our message across with the least words possible, this can be painstakingly difficult. Similar to sensate focus, the value of slowing down allows for a deeper connection and experience. So much of what we do is s.l.o.w.i.n.g d.o.w.n in all the ways. Being present with our bodies, ourselves and, eventually, with the other person is what makes a great friend and lover.

Finally, being with our clients in a public setting can be a beautiful way to bring all the pieces together. They receive the opportunity to try out real life with me! They soon learn how many details are at play when going out to dinner, for example:

- what time to arrive before the date
- where to sit
- how to hold space for the date
- their needs
- figuring out what to order
- matching it with their date
- how to communicate who is paying
- and dozens of other things

While many of these details may matter to their date, how they approach it with their date matters more. It is an opportunity for the client to learn what works for them and what doesn't and what they can learn about the other person too. It's not about perfection and precision but how to be present and available to whatever happens in the moment.

Some specific requests have been made to meet their needs that round out the socialization package. Posture, walking, slow dancing, selfie-taking, and texting can all be part of what we include in time with our clients. Each client can dive in where they believe they need additional support.

Ultimately, we want our clients to walk confidently back into their lives, fully present and aware of their sensual/sexual self-confidence, after our time ends, managing everything with attention and intention. It's impossible to predict and address what they'll need in their future socially, but if they can remember to come from the place of "You with You," and to speak authentically from their experience, ask for what they need and want, be open to feedback from friends and lovers, and slow down, they'll be able to create the future they want.

Reflections of You with Others

1) Do you feel it would be helpful to teach young folks early on about dating and relationship skills? Why?

2) What skills, thinking back, do you wish you'd had before being thrown into the ring?

3) Dancing, communication, asking permission, dating... in which categories would you have appreciated at least the Cliff Notes?

4) Would it be of value for schools to start teaching social skills when we are young and just beginning the journey outside the safety of home?

Thoughts & Quotes

The hypocrisy around the subject of sexuality is

huge. Early on, there were others who were a lot more interested in you satisfying what made them feel good than in satisfying what made you feel good. There were so many things that you felt inclined to go this way, that you were forced to go that way, that at an early age, you made a conscious decision that if it felt good, it was wrong. And if it felt wrong, it was probably right. - dailyquote@abraham-hicks.com

"We all have scars, we gonna have more. Rather than struggle against time and waste it, let's dance with time and redeem it. Cause we don't live longer when we try not to die. We live longer when we are too busy living."

— Matthew McConaughey, Greenlights

Chapter Nine Out of Touch

"The reality is that we are bodies born of other bodies,

bodies feeding other bodies,

bodies having sex with other bodies,

bodies seeking a shoulder to lean or cry on….

bodies matter, which is why anything

related to them arouses emotions."

- Frans DE Waal, *Our Inner Ape*

~*~

Our Most Basic Need: Touch. The Way Back to our Humanity

Within this theme, I speak to the fact that touch is our

most developed sense when we are born and the one that never changes as we age. Also addressed is the fact that we, with ourselves, our relationships, our country, our world are... out of touch. What did folks experience during the Covid-19 pandemic in 2020, when touch was basically illegal? How did we feel? What did we learn?

The most important guidelines to be acknowledged around touch are permission and consent. Understanding the difference between these two requirements provides both toucher and touchee healthy, respectful, and mutually welcomed connection. There is a language, both spoken and unspoken, that distinguishes the how and why we give and the how and why we receive.

We begin to form our ideas, thoughts, and beliefs about ourselves and others—including security, the world, relationships, being close to others, being held, and reaching out for our parents—the minute we are born.

We need touch to thrive, as it is our most developed

sense when we are born, and the one that stays with us as we age. When it is missing from our early lives, or is scarce, we notice. Over time, without our being aware, it can change our behavior and expectations, which will have an impact on us as we grow. People in the LGBTQIA population may be lacking in healthy, nurturing touch, given the social, familial, or religious rejection and discrimination they face. Withholding of love and acceptance is so often experienced by queer people. It's important to understand and address these barriers, because healthy touch is a powerful way to foster emotional, mental, and physical well-being.

Is it Consent or Permission?

I'd like to redefine consent. The dictionary describes consent as agreeing to do something or allowing someone else to do something. By consenting, you agree to something someone else wants: "I consent to X." If you say, "give consent" or "get consent" this is what you are talking about. I'd like to expand the definition and think of consent as an agreement that two or more people come up with together. You don't give consent.... you arrive at consent together...

~*~

People often confuse consent with permission. When there is something you want to do that affects someone else, permission is what you need. It starts with "May I....?"

~*~

If you have a hard time asking for what you want or setting limits it brings to light the difference between Want-to and Willing-to, between doing something for yourself and doing something for the other person, and more. Because of all thi smy understanding of consent has become broader and more specific.

A schoolteacher described consent for kids. "If the other person is not enjoying it, you have to stop." With adults it's the same with the added layer of who it's for...

~*~

Based on working with the Wheel of Consent, I have come to see consent skills as:

*Noticing what you want, asking for it, and abiding by the answer

*Noticing the difference between what you want and what you are willing to give and communicate that.

*Finding out what the other person wants and what the other person is okay with and distinguishing between those two.

*Abiding by your agreement even when things move quickly or get exciting

*Being able to abide by someone's no or limits.

*Being able to change your mind and making room for the other person to change theirs.

For much more about Consent, I recommend, Betty Martin, D.C. Author: *The Art of Receiving and Giving* and learning about The Wheel of Consent

Unwanted Touch/Consent

If touch is a language, it seems we would instinctively know how to use it. But, apparently, it is an inborn skill that needs to be nurtured and supported. Subjects in one study consistently understated their ability to communicate via touch, which is even more effective than talking or facial expressions, in conveying emotion.

When you are touched by another person, your brain is not set up to give you the objective qualities of that touch. The entire experience is affected by your early messages and social evaluation of the person touching you.

When we are touching someone or being touched, we want to be certain that it is a wanted exchange of the required feel-good hormones.

Welcome or Unwelcome Touch – How Do I Know or Show My Consent?

Many folks can relate to a teenage movie scenario. A

teen couple sits in a theater on a first date. He is nervous but curious as he raises his hand to his mouth in a fake yawn and stretches that arm around his date's shoulders. Neither says a word. He wonders, "Is this okay?" She wonders, "Is this okay?" She feels embarrassed and is unable to tell her date whether his touch is welcome.

Having trouble determining how to understand and handle nonconsensual touch?

Take a look at the work of Betty Martin: www.BettyMartin.org. The Wheel of Consent page has nine free hours of introduction and instructions. Also, check out Betty's book: *The Art of Receiving and Giving: The Wheel of Consent*. It is available on Amazon.com.

Covid-19 and Our New Reality

The Covid-19 pandemic taught us firsthand what happens and what it feels like when touch is basically illegal. Because of Covid-19, we had to be aware of medical concerns associated with touching and hugging, and we had to figure out how to say hello, how to say goodbye, and even how to be near our loved ones. During this time, we have learned various ways to express hello, goodbye, I am glad to see you, I honor you and appreciate our friendship: bowing, hand to heart, prayerful hands to heart, fist bump, high five. There is now an awareness of being respectful and asking for permission to touch. This applies to all types of relationships: friends, acquaintances, a first meeting, or people who have been married for thirty years. We now have a respect for the other's "space."

How do we accept or feel comfortable asking for consent? Back to the early messages of touch. We are often trained as children to accept unwanted touch. Remember the family gatherings where you were forced to "go kiss Aunt Hattie"? Or had to sit on Uncle Frank's lap? This conditioning begins in childhood, and we sometimes struggle with our autonomy because it becomes wired in (like our first kiss memory).

With unwanted touch, we must take on that established wiring and learn so we can set new, healthy boundaries with the old and new people in our lives. We couldn't set boundaries as children, but we can and must as adults. Once these healthy boundaries are set, we need to explain them to the people in our lives and stick to them.

The Concept of Touch Beyond the Physical

Touch beyond the physical affects us emotionally, mentally, and psychologically. The emotional importance of our sense of touch runs deep. We are social beings who need others around us to experience fulfillment. Loneliness has severe consequences for health and well-being. Research, both qualitative and quantitative, has demonstrated that a most important piece of human heritage is the need for physical contact. From birth to death, our sense of touch never changes.

Touch has been known to help with learning

disabilities, developmental disabilities, and learning in general. These are called skin/brain messages. Studies have even demonstrated that hugs help us brave winter and not suffer from colds and flu viruses. In the next section, we will speak about more research findings around cardiovascular diseases, aging and loneliness, and babies thriving or dying due to touch or touch deprivation.

We will look at the science of touch, the nervous system, and the endocrine system, which releases neurotransmitters and chemical hormones. The hormone oxytocin is well known as it promotes feel-good sensations that we remember from childhood on into adulthood.

~*~

My colleague Rae Lee Stegall, a sex coach and expert scientific consultant, and I recently taught a course on Touch Beyond the Physical. Here is what Rae presented about the science of touch:

When we touch someone's arm during physical skin contact, what is happening? Besides the epidermal surface touch, we are impacting the body's electrical nervous system as well as the endocrine system, which releases neurotransmitters and brain chemical hormones. So, touch has a multilevel impact on many overlying systems of the body.

Science continues to prove the many positive health manifestations from touch as it increases your happiness and longevity, while reducing your social anxiety and stress. Physical touch is proven to boost the immune system and lower blood pressure. This is because touch is an intrinsic human need, and we wither in its absence because it is vital to our well-being as human beings. Early touch helps provide the template for all relationships thereafter.

This is most outwardly witnessed in cases of infants and children in orphanages who are deprived of touch and then fail to thrive and die, but this is happening to all ages on subtle and not so subtle levels. Researchers discovered touch is vital, as babies who are not held and snuggled enough would stop growing altogether and eventually die. Before this was recently understood, orphanages had infant mortality rates 30-40 percent, but some were 100 percent. The children that do make it out alive are left with over 30 percent higher rates of psychiatric disorders than children without such a history (53.2 percent versus 22.0 percent).[1]

Touch has been shown to help with school, as a study found that students are three times as likely to speak up in class after their teacher pats them in a friendly way. Even more impressive is the fact that after positive touching, a 60 percent reduction in disruptive behavior was seen compared with the average of such behavior before the tactile encouragement.[2, 3] Mirroring these results of the positive effects of touching was found with elderly people within the framework of proposed manual tasks.[2,4]

Hugs keep you healthy and are a behavioral indicator of support and intimacy. A social support and hugging study conducted at Carnegie Mellon University revealed an apparent protective effect of hugs that those who received hugs often or on a regular basis experienced far less cold/flu symptoms than participants who did not get as many hugs. Regular hugs lower and buffer stress levels in our body and therefore reduce susceptibility to catching infectious diseases such as colds and viruses.[5]

A study titled *Loneliness Matters: A Theoretical and Empirical Review of Consequences and Mechanisms* was a compiled review regarding social relations and health, which showed:

- Loneliness has been associated with personality disorders and psychosis, suicide, impaired and deteriorative cognitive performance, a significantly increased risk of Alzheimer's disease, diminished executive control, and increases in depressive symptoms.

- The risk of suffering from cardiovascular health risk in young adulthood (twenty-six years old) is higher with people who experienced chronic social isolation or rejection during childhood and youth.

- Chronic high-frequency loneliness in women was associated with incident coronary heart disease.

- There is a connection between loneliness and depression with adverse health outcomes.

- Loneliness was associated with increased systolic blood pressure in a population-based sample of middle-aged adults.

- With retired elderly people, chronic loneliness is the most accurate indicator for mortality and life duration.

- Loneliness heightens feelings of vulnerability and unconscious vigilance for social threat, implicit cognitions that are antithetical to relaxation and sound sleep.

- Self-reported poor sleep quality leads to daytime dysfunction.

- Loneliness has been associated with impaired cellular immunity as reflected in lower natural killer (NK) cell activity.

- In young adults, loneliness was associated with poorer antibody response to a component of the flu vaccine.

> • In sum, feelings of loneliness mark increased risk for morbidity and mortality, a phenomenon that arguably reflects the social essence of our species.[6]

On the other end of the spectrum, a study of the results of nurturing touch revealed that a mother's love affects the volume of her child's hippocampus. Brain images of children with nurturing mothers revealed hippocampal volumes 10 percent larger than those of children whose mothers were not as nurturing. Research has suggested a link between a larger hippocampus and better memory. Other studies also found a connection between early social experiences and the volume of the amygdala, which helps regulate the processing and memory of emotional reactions.[7]

I think touching someone's skin is like touching their brain. The brain and nervous system have multiple neurotransmitters that regulate many important bodily functions and mental states, and they respond to a nurturing human touch. So, you can soothe the brain. Touch unlocks the health of our nervous system and thus our entire mind-body connection.

The hormone oxytocin is another benefit of physical touch and cuddling. It helps humans connect to others and promotes feel-good sensations that foster a sense of well-being and happiness. And this stimulates the release of other feel-good hormones such as dopamine and serotonin. The hormones cortisol and adrenaline can be released in the presence of unwanted touch, which can also trigger a flight, fight, or fawn response.

Let's focus on bringing more oxytocin to the world, it inspires the best in people, including enhancing positive thinking, expanding trust, creates bonding, and generates compassion during social situations.[8]

In my work I find clients are struggling as they reach and stretch to find those places that say internally that they are of value, for they are being deprived of the most basic of our biological needs, which is to be touched. One of the hardest sensate focus exercises is called the mirror exercise. Here they stand before the mirror, first fully clothed, and they are asked to report their relationship with their body. Some folks just stand there and cry. Again, our relationship of You with You is of primary importance. Do we stand up for ourselves in allowing only consensual touch? Do we show respect for others' autonomy in our giving of touch? The "skin-brain" knows, and it is with us from birth to death.

In the 1980's song by Dan Hill: "Sometimes when we touch, the honesty's too much, and I have to close my eyes and hide. I'm only just beginning to see the real you. I want to hold you till I die, till we both break down and cry. I want to hold you till the fear in me subsides."

The depth of a touch, the fear of really being known. "I'm only just beginning to see the real you". Touch is the pathway to Plain Damn You. It is the pathway to the deepest connection of You with You and You with Others. "At times I'd like to break through and hold you endlessly." Thank you, Dan Hill @danhill.com

References:

[1] Zeanah CH, Egger HL, Smyke AT, Nelson CA, Fox NA, Marshall PJ, & Guthrie D. Institutional rearing and psychiatric disorders in Romanian preschool children. *Am J Psychiatry*. 2009 Jul; 166(7):777–85.

[2] Guéguen, Nicolas. Nonverbal encouragement of participation in a course: the effect of touching. Social Psychology of Education. 2004. 7: 89–98.

[3] Wheldall, Kevin, Bevan, Kate, & Shortall, Kath (1986) A touch of reinforcement: the effects of contingent teacher touch on the classroom behaviour of young children, *Educational Review*, 38:3, 207–216

[4] Howard, D. (1988). The effects of touch in the geriatric population. *Physical and Occupational Therapy in Geriatrics*, 6, 35–50.

[5] Cohen, S., Janicki-Deverts, D., Turner, R., & Doyle, W. (2014). Does hugging provide stress-buffering social support? A study of susceptibility to upper respiratory infection and illness. *Psychological Science.* https://pubmed.ncbi.nlm.nih.gov/25526910/

[6] Hawkley, LC., & Cacioppo, J. T. (2010). Loneliness matters: A theoretical and empirical review of consequences and mechanisms. *Annals of Behavioral Medicine*, 40(2), 218–227.

[7] Luby JL, Barch DM, Belden A, Gaffrey MS, Tillman R, Babb C, Nishino T, Suzuki H, & Botteron KN. Maternal support in early childhood predicts larger hippocampal volumes at school age. *Proceedings of the National Academy of Sciences Early Edition*, Jan. 30, 2012.

[8] Ishak WW, Kahloon M, & Fakhry H. Oxytocin role in enhancing well-being: A literature review. *Journal of Affective Disorders*. 2011;130(1):1–9

Cliches About "Touch"

- Reach out and touch someone
- Stay in touch
- Let's touch base
- Out of touch
- Touch and go
- Touch of class
- Add a touch of sugar
- Touched in the head, etc.
- Touch someone's life
- One Touch (appliance)
- Touch down
- Touch up
- Don't touch that

~*~

I was interviewed on Nikki Leigh's *Ready for Love Radio* show to discuss touch. You can hear it at this link - https://podcasts.bcast.fm/e/xn1q4pjn

Appendix B includes Ancient Seneca Wisdom about Touch from Grandmother Twylah.Hurd Nitsch.

The Power of Touch by Dr. Patti Britton on The Boomalicious Life - https://drpattibritton.com/episodes/episode-11-the-power-of-touch/

Sometimes When We Touch by Dan Hill - https://www.youtube.com/watch?v=IATz8ZVTALo

Reflections of You with Others

1) Reach out and touch someone...with permission, of course. Do you find there are confusing and ambiguous messages about when and when not to touch? How could this be improved?

2) Is physical touch the only way to be touched? How else can you identify being "touched"?

3) Does touch give you a sense of your own value? Why do you feel that way?

4) Is touch something you avoid? Are there reasons why you feel that way? When did this disconnect happen?

Thoughts and Quotes

QUIRKY FACT: An adult-sized skin bag stretched out would range to around twenty square feet.

~*~

"If you are touched by something it makes you feel sad, sympathetic, or grateful." – Betty Martin

~*~

Touch has a memory - John Keats

~*~

"Too often we underestimate the power of a touch… which has the potential to turn a life around. - Leo Buscaglia

~*~

"The world is small but are we in touch." – Matthew McConaughey

~*~

"To be able to feel the lightest touch really is a gift." - Christopher Reeves

Thirds Theory

of

Self-Actualization

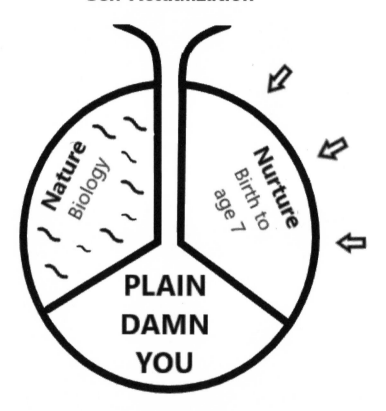

The Thirds Theory expands on the Maslow's Hierarchy of Needs model by digging deeper into how Nature, Nurture, and Plain Damn You develops self-actualized adults.

Chapter Ten Plain Damn You

"Do what you feel in your heart to be right - for you will be criticized anyway. You will be damned if you do and damned if you don't." - Eleanor Roosevelt

Inside the question of... Am I Normal If... came the question of what is natural for you. After having looked at your first five years, religious training, early messages, relationship firsts, and understanding of touch, we now have the "thread" that leads us to the big-picture awareness of You with You that gives us a road map to Plain Damn You. What does it feel like? Can we proceed to the bigger piece of your puzzle... Am I Natural If? This leads to the question of what's "natural" for you, and who is better qualified to determine that than you?

Consider this. Does this question, this possibility, this quest to explore your own nature and nurture give you the motivation to honor your desires, your reason to get out of bed, your being on the planet? What could be a deep philosophical discussion is boiled down to this: who is Plain Damn You? Is the You with You, your snowflake, your fingerprint, your unique contribution to humanity being allowed to shine and to be respected?

Finding and figuring out just *WHO* Plain Damn You really is became the central guide and a major key for the journey each client embarks on in the search that is guided by their commitment to their body, mind, wholeness, and ultimately their healthy sexuality.

In the early 2000s, the question of whether people are gay because of their nurturing or because of their nature, which is the biology of past generations, came to the forefront. My answer: What if it is just who they are? Thus, was created my Thirds Theory: Nature, Nurture, Plain Damn You. Hence this book you hold in your hands. This theory evolved as the question expanded from why is someone gay? to the myriad of universal questions surrounding Am I Normal If?

How boring to have just one species of flower, one color in the rainbow, one variety of tree, etc. Why is the "should" of humanity that "normal" means we all are the same color, speak the same language, heed the same religions, have the same beliefs, etc. etc.

Diversity solves one aspect of the "am I normal if." Once we realize we are all snowflakes, have our own unique fingerprint and DNA, we can move from the prison of being "normal," which is more comfortable than one size fits all. Diversity invites creativity and thinking outside the box. When experiencing culturally diverse connections, we expand our acceptance of ourselves and others for the gifts we bring with our own special contributions. Because of this, we are healthier, both mentally and emotionally, as we see each of us as one individual. This is why, like nature, we need diversity.

The box called "normal," which changes with time and includes fashion, politics, religion, and everything else, became the quest in my therapy and my teachings for a connection to who am I? Outside the box of normal, what are the gifts, talents, and unique imprint I bring to this spinning top we call the world? What is the fingerprint that only I can contribute to the global experience? The answer begins with your acceptance (which is love) for yourself and honoring *Plain Damn You*. That is *how* you make a difference. If you fit in the box called "normal," there is a loss to yourself and humanity.

Each day in my office with my clients, there is one consistent message: they ask me some variation of "Am I normal if..." This seems to be a very pervasive human concern. We all want to know if we meet the invisible set of standards. We're not asking if we're just like everyone else, but do we fit in?

There are things about ourselves that we don't share with anyone, not our brothers or sisters or even our closest friends. We feel vulnerable sharing certain aspects of our thoughts, desires, and actions that make us different, or strange... or maybe, by chance, do they make us like other people who also carry hidden pieces of themselves?

Throughout the pages of this book, we have discussed the pieces that I use to work with my clients. I dig into each client's past to find the threads that make up the details we need to make a profound difference in their life. It is amazing to go back—all the way back to the beginning, even before birth, and take a look at the things that influenced them, their relationship with themself, with their family. I take a look at their religion, early sexual messages, early sexual experiences, early trauma, first sexual intercourse—all that and much more can impact all the steppingstones of the intimacy and relationships in their journey.

To understand these fascinating details about you, we start with what I call my Thirds Theory. I'll explain it in detail, and we will get to know this tool intimately. This tool helps us to prepare to meet Plain Damn You!

What Is "Plain Damn You"?

How do you find Plain Damn You? When I begin

work with a new client, we start with a pen and a piece of paper. I want you to get out a piece of paper and draw a peace sign like the one below.

Thirds Theory
of
Self-Actualization

From the top of the circle, draw a line down and two lines off the bottom. On the top left section of the circle, there is a big chunk. Inside that section, that third is your "nature." That's what you get through your biology. The genetics, the now-known science of "epigenetics." This is the biology you arrive with and which you have no control over.

Now move over to the third on the right side. Write in that third "nurture" and draw little arrows outside the circle pointing in toward the circle, because that's the people and things that come from the outside and affect you. It includes who you were born to, where you grew up, where you went to school, what religion you were raised with, or were there no religious teachings? The question of whether you were nurtured or not. You know, all those things that came in, which we, again, had no control over. These things had a large impact on you when you were young and impressionable. Many people started rebelling as teenagers, and all hell started to break loose because Plain Damn You was trying to come on board!

In the bottom third of your peace sign is what I call Plain Damn You, because that's your unique fingerprint, your individualized snowflake. It's the gift you came in with, and the lessons you came to learn, that created the unique YOU. Draw two lines up, from the point at the bottom of the triangle, straight through nature and nurture and extend them outside the circle. You've got something like a tube that comes up from Plain Damn You through nature and nurture. At the top of that, write "Self-Actualized Adult," because when people come to me, that's what this whole thing is about, THEIR "normal." We dig to excavate what is "normal and natural" for them. We uncover and discover by either embracing or discarding each piece they unearth from their nature or nurture, discarding the things that do not serve their box called Plain Damn Me!

Let's look at what's natural for you, as we walk through finding the Plain Damn You inside your nature/nurture. I have everybody go home with one of these drawings and put it on their bathroom mirror. I tell them, "When you're making a decision about something, I want you to look at this and ask yourself if the decision is coming from the biology/nature or the nurturing or the YOU with YOU?"

Sometimes a client may say my grandfather was an alcoholic, my father is an alcoholic, and my brother is an alcoholic, I don't want to be an alcoholic. So, you throw alcoholism out because this biology doesn't serve you. Or another client who was religious as a child and was told by the church that sex is dirty, wrong, sinful, and evil. The church says you have to deny the body and things like that. This client thinks, I don't want to follow that. I think bodies are beautiful and should be treated with respect and responsibility. We can be in charge and in control of our bodies. This is the goal: growing up through the nature and the nurture and growing INTO your own *self-actualized adult* to reach multiple layers of growth and development.

We are all subjected to the "shoulds" of our families, the "shoulds" of society, the "shoulds" of religion, the "shoulds" of our communities, the "shoulds" of our friends, the "shoulds" that can change daily or with every change in fads or in the political arena. These so-called "normals" can follow us throughout our lives. Through my work, I help people look at who *they* are, what *they* want, NOT who they are *supposed* to be biologically or according to their upbringing. Instead, we look at mental, emotional, and physical health when we start honoring and putting more importance on our own individuality.

We're expected to fit in and "play the game" like everyone else. If we're "different" in any way or "weird," people feel the need to judge us. People who dare to ask questions or move outside the mainstream are vilified and bullied for their actions and life choices. For some reason—especially in the United States, for a host of reasons—people can't seem to just "live and let live."

This is especially true in the world of sexuality. It is one of the most controlled and judged areas in society. That's why I ask questions about who raised you, did they love each other, did they love you and, very importantly, did you feel that they loved you, and was there religion in the home? Religion can really set people apart from being able to love themselves and others. I ask what was your first masturbation experience, were you caught, did your family find out, and did they shame you? These are early foundational experiences that lead people to struggle with connecting to themselves from the neck down in a healthy, positive way.

One example: Mom and Dad are upstairs, and you're on the couch with your girlfriend having sex. You're trying to hurry up and get done before they come downstairs. This "hurry up and get done" mentality at a young age sets both of you up for problems, at that time and in later life, in your sexual experiences and interactions. One major category of our clients' concerns is premature ejaculation. These early experiences get hardwired into your physical, emotional, and mental memory.

For women, your first time could have been horrible because you might have bled all over the place, you were embarrassed, it hurt, and it was likely over before you got started. Then you spent twenty to thirty years figuring out how to have sex you enjoy or, more commonly, can live with and accept, while being disappointed with your sex life. Or, for too many women—who are still hearing those outdated comments that it's "your duty" to have sex—you don't speak up and tell him what you like or don't like, because you will hurt his fragile male ego. Then there are religious messages that deny women pleasure: you're not supposed to enjoy sex so you have no idea what you may like about sex, or it is your duty to have children and then you can stop having sex, and on and on.

Why Am I Sharing This Book with YOU?

I think this struggle with "normal" affects everyone, and many are affected deeply, as well as on the surface. What is "normal"? *I think just feeling you're not abnormal doesn't solve the whole issue.* Normal and abnormal, who gets to say, who decides? You can walk up to one person and say, "Am I normal?" They can say, "Sure, wear what you want and do what you want."

You walk up to two people and say, "Am I normal if I like to wear plaid?" One says yes, and one says no.

Does that make you normal or abnormal?

Does that make them normal or abnormal?

Or… does it make us all *individuals*?

That word "normal" has such a stigma connected to it, but so many people crave it so much. Or, maybe they just fear the idea of being abnormal, so by default they feel they need to find out how to fit in… with everybody!

What if we switch the goal to "natural" and instead we look at mother nature? Nature just has a natural way of being very diverse, and there is no "what if." There's just a prescribed way of being exactly who you are… your own original and unique snowflake… or… Plain Damn You.

Dr. Susan Kaye

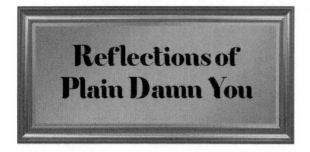

Reflections of Plain Damn You

1) Can you relate to this "box" called normal? How has it affected you?

2) Does Plain Damn You make you feel more powerful or vulnerable? Explain your answer.

3) Are there early foundational messages that led you to struggle with being able to connect with yourself?

4) Being exactly who you are sometimes takes courage. Are you up for the challenge?

Thoughts and Quotes

"People come in many shapes, sizes, ages, genders, ethnicities, skin tones, and other differences. That doesn't make us unacceptable or abnormal, it makes us individuals!" – Nikki Leigh, Love & Relationship Coach and Host of Ready for Love Radio

~*~

"I am what I am…" – Popeye, Fictional Character

~*~

"Today is the perfect day to start living your dreams." –Unknown

~*~

"Until a person can say deeply and honestly, "I am what I am today because of the choices I made yesterday," that person cannot say, "I choose otherwise." – Stephen R. Covey

~*~

"What we call our destiny is truly our character and that character can be altered." - Anais Nin

~*~

"What you do every day matters more than what you do once in a while." - Gretchen Rubin

~*~

"When you repeat a mistake, it's no longer a mistake. It's a decision." - Paulo Coelho

~*~

"You are essentially who you create yourself to be and all that occurs in your life is the result of your own making." – Stephen Richards

~*~

"You are never too old to set another goal or to dream a new dream." – C.S. Lewis

~*~

"You cannot always be strong, but you can always be brave." -Beau Taplin

Chapter Eleven Nature and Nurture Creates Diversity

"My dream is for all gender non-conforming kids, youth and adults to be understood not as unusual or pathological, but, viewed through a lens of reverence and respect, as valued members of the human race."

- Dr. Michele Angello

~*~

"Many people find it easy to judge others, based on their appearance or other superficial things. In this chapter many different sorts of people are included and explanations are provided. Dr. Kaye has worked with individuals like these and many more and you may be able to relate to their stories. Each of us are individuals with our own stories, our own struggles, and our own uniqueness. Our goal with this chapter is to help people appreciate that individualism and uniqueness in themselves and others, instead of using it to judge, belittle or harass people who are

different. I think the world would be boring if everyone was alike. I love being unique. You should try it!" – Nikki Leigh, Author, Editor, Certified Love & Relationship Coach

~*~

Roget's II The New Thesaurus:

Nature (noun): character, disposition, essence, kind

Nurture (verb): to promote and sustain the development of

At birth there are two boxes society thinks we should "fit" into, and they are defined by these two words.

Nature: he is just like his father and his grandfather before him.

Nurture: what do you expect, look where she was born.

Messages and assumptions such as these follow us into adulthood *if* we *allow* ourselves to be pigeonholed, labeled, and demeaned by such limited potential.

Who we are born to and where we are born and grow up is the foundation from which we build our own springboard. Choosing the goal and our outcome is up to us. This is the beginning of our opportunity to "know thyself." The mystery and wonder of "who will I be, how will I expand the possibility of these ingredients into a life I choose?" Will you take the baton of ancestry and the circumstances you were given and choose you? "Your assignment...should you accept it."

"So often times it happens that we live our lives in chains, and never even know we have the key." Glen Frey, The Eagles

~*~

In 2000 I received my PhD and began teaching in a community college. It was around this time the question arose: Why are people gay? Myriads of discussions, conclusions, and questions were in the news; in the tabloids; and on the desks of scientists, biologists, parents and, most of all, the folks who were walking with "am I normal if?" Students, of course, felt the "sex teacher," me, would have a simple answer. This is when "Plain Damn You" was born. I walked to the blackboard—yes, I was still using a blackboard—and drew the peace sign. This symbolizes who a person is: one-third is biology (nature), one-third is your upbringing (nurture), and one-third is You...your fingerprint or, as I like to say, your snowflake, lessons, gifts...Plain Damn You.

These questions also led me to study and understand more clearly the x/y chromosome variations.

Chromosomal Differences

X and Y variations, known medically as sex chromosome aneuploidy (SCA), involve variations in the typical number and type of sex chromosomes. The typical number of chromosomes in each human cell is forty-six. These include twenty-two pairs of "autosomes" (which refers to all chromosomes that are not sex chromosomes) and a pair of sex chromosomes: either an X and a Y, which make a male, or two Xs, which make a female. That means the genetic signature for a person with forty-six chromosomes is either 46,XY (male), or 46,XX (female).

Any variation from these numbers is referred to scientifically as an "aneuploidy." If there is one additional X or Y, it is known as a "trisomy" ("tri" denoting the number three). Several of the more common genetic conditions that reflect a trisomy include:

- 47,XXY (Klinefelter syndrome)
- 47,XXX (Trisomy X)
- 47,XYY (Sometimes known as Jacob's syndrome)

https://genetic.org/wp-content/uploads/2018/08/AXYS-Brochure-General-2018.pdf

At the other end of the spectrum lie the "monosomies," meaning a person is born with only one sex chromosome. The only survivable monosomy SCA is 45,X. This is a female with only one X chromosome, a condition known as "Turner syndrome." A fetus with only one Y chromosome and no X chromosome is not viable and cannot survive.

Sex chromosome aneuploidy is not inherited. The extra chromosome is the result of an error that occurs in cell division when the egg or sperm is formed, or occasionally during cell division after fertilization. An extra X can be contributed by either the mother or father. Only the father can contribute an extra Y chromosome.

We all begin as females (see the chart below). *Our Sexuality*, 10th Edition by Robert Crooks and Karla Baur, pages 50 and 51.

Hormones working at their optimum level leads to full differentiation. If not working at the optimal level, anomalies occur.

Early Human External Genital Development

"The external genitals develop in a similar pattern, resembling female until the gonads begin releasing

DHT hormones during the 6th week. It is then the external genital tissues of males and females become differentiated. DHT stimulates the outer labia swelling to drop down and become the scrotum, the inner labia folds to differentiate into the shaft of the penis. These genital folds fuse around the urethra to form the shaft of the penis and the clitoris swells to form the penis foreskin and head."

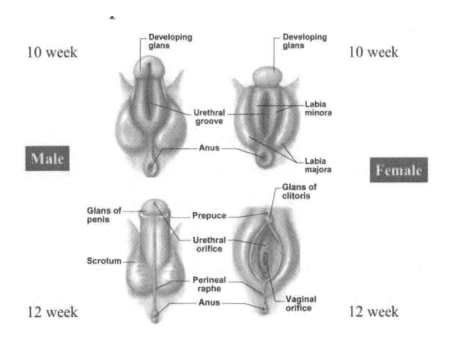

(Image from - https://www.lifewithgremlins.com/when-can-you-tell-the-gender-of-a-baby-external-gender-development/)

As you can see, nature tends toward females. In the absence of testosterone, or if the DHT does not process at the *exact* right time, possibly under the influence of a foreign substance or substances, anomalies occur. Conditions experienced by clients I have met as a body practitioner include: intersexed when born with ambiguous genitalia; bladder exstrophy when the baby is full-term; and normal birth, but hips are splayed and genital area is like jelly and on the outside. The genitalia has to be reconstructed, and it is easier to make a hole than a pole. (Meaning it is easier to *make* the baby a girl than a boy.)

"Bladder exstrophy is a congenital abnormality that occurs when the skin over the lower abdominal wall (bottom part of the tummy) does not form properly. The bladder is open and exposed on the outside of the abdomen. In epispadias, the urethra does not form properly. Exstrophy means "turned inside out." (same resource as above)

There is also the sex differentiation of the brain and hormones. We know so much more now regarding genes, chromosomes, brain chemicals, hormones, and all the other ingredients that make up the soup that is you. And this is just barely scratching the surface of the differences there are that happen naturally. We cannot put people in the "normal box" without going against nature. Then, yes, there is nurture, but what is most important is what is "natural" for you… Plain Damn You!

Diversity of GSRD

"In regards to our sexuality, a new concept that has come to my attention from the British Social Science Circle is the umbrella term of Gender and Sexual Relationship Diversity (GSRD)," Dr Meg-John Barker, Writer, Therapist, and Activist specializing in GSRD. (https://counsellorneil.co.uk/sexuality/)

The term GSRD encompasses a multitude of gender expressions, sexual orientations, and relationship types. It more broadly includes marginalized groups who might not find themselves well represented under the title of LGBTQIA+. Essentially, labeling someone by their sexuality is limited, since we are so much more diverse than what gender we choose to connect with intimately.

This lack of representation is why the word "queer" has been added to LGBTQ as a catch-all for those who do not fall into one of the boxes. In contrast, the term GSRD covers not only individual sexual orientations but their gender identities and what types of relationships they might be interested in pursuing. In this way, it leaves space for relationships and identities who are not included in LGBTQ, and it does not force people to fit themselves into a category, but rather allows for freedom to describe all relationship diversities. Even someone who might appear heterosexual to the outside world can be included in this umbrella if they have a unique gender identity or a non-normative relationship style.

For example, someone may be assumed to be heterosexual, but actually their partner is nonbinary, or a couple might be both cisgender and heterosexual but practice ethical nonmonogamy with people of more diverse gender identities. Another example is someone who identifies as asexual but homoromantic, and they carry on relationships but not sexual ones. This is where the GSRD can be used to shift the stigma around being labeled LGBTQ+ to acknowledge that most relationships can involve different kinds of diversity. It is important also because not everyone should need to describe what kind of people they like to sexually engage with to describe their identity or the style of relationship they are seeking.

When someone uses GSRD to describe their orientation, it provides many more options to them. It allows for flexibility of gender, sexual orientation, and relationship style. This, in turn, allows folks to more accurately state what they are seeking from a partner. It also is a more succinct way to include the smorgasbord of identities that exist in the world instead of continually adding letters to the same old acronym: LGBTQIAA2+.

Though historically surrogacy focused on helping cisgender, heterosexual males, it has come a long way to expand and embrace modern relationship diversity. Surrogacy was developed in the 1960s but attained more recognition in the '70s and '80s. In the '90s, when homosexuality was no longer illegal and seen as a mental disorder, there began to be options for LGBTQIA individuals to seek same-sex surrogate partners and clients. Previously, those seeking surrogacy particularly because of their gender identity or sexual orientation had been kept from this therapeutic process of developing fulfilling sexual and emotional relationships. In my career, I have worked with several surrogates who focused on the gay male population and lesbians as well.

It is only in the last fifteen to twenty years that we in the mental and physical health community have been able to acknowledge the pain and trauma that our clients have in relating to their own gender identities and sexual or relationship orientations. In this way, the work I do can be strongly tied to how people embody their gender and what wounds they carry from being taught that their gender or sexual identity is wrong, broken, immoral, or does not even exist.

Crossdressers and Transgender People

Crossdressers and trans folks have also been and still are our clients. Many of these folks live their lives in secrecy, hiding these seemingly simple desires for fear that they will not be able to have healthy partnerships, obtain and hold jobs, or have families that accept their "unique" Plain Damn You! Instead, this fear and self-denial lead to a deep need for both "neck up" and "neck down" work. We have taken our clients to personal clothing consultants, hairstylists, and makeup specialists and taught them how to walk in high heels. We support and walk with them in telling their families, telling their employers' human resources departments, and through pre and post surgeries. With wraparound support, our clients can accept their own gender identities, sexual orientations, and relationship styles, which impacts their ability to create strong and secure relationships with themselves and intimate partners.

Working with the Intellectually Disabled

My first job out of college, in 1992, with a BA in human services, was as a sexuality consultant for the developmentally disabled (called today ID or intellectually disabled). I was hired by Northwest Human Services, which was funded by the County of Philadelphia. My role was mostly to stop males from masturbating in public and to assist staff in managing the behaviors of those who were assigned constant supervision due to potential sexual offenses.

What I quickly learned from the residents, who mostly lived in male-designated and female-designated group homes, was that they wanted to have the opportunity to connect in significant-other relationships. They wanted to date, to have someone to hold hands with and one client wrote: "Dr. Kaye, I would like someone to write Christmas cards to."

I began a campaign to obtain funding for social events. We held dance parties, bowling outings, and picnics. We also held dinner and a movie night for our couples. We had one couple in our group who were able to marry. House parents had to take their hetero males to clubs where they could meet women.

Our gay and lesbian folks attended Philadelphia's Gay Pride Parade, and my cross-dressers were taken to local thrift shops to purchase earrings, purses, and appropriate clothing to match their gender identity. When I left in 2002, there were programs in place to continue this very important work, which gave people with special needs the diversity to provide a feeling of normally and naturally living in their skin.

Asperger's and Autism

In my practice, I've worked with clients who walked with Asperger's and autism. Some used wheelchairs, had multiple medical issues, and lived in rehabs because of traumatic brain injury (TBI). We saw so many miraculous results in folks who were seen as asexual. Human beings who are interested in dating, connecting with a partner, or possibly even marriage. Their questions are humanity's core questions: Am I Normal If... Can I have, for myself, the basic need to be loved and accepted for who I am, regardless of how I am perceived or labeled as not being natural or normal by other people.

I still get a Christmas card from Robert, who lives with very open parents who allowed him to attend our parties, dances, and bowling events. He signs his cards Love, Robert. Each card reminds me of the value of diversity and uniqueness. He is an out-of-the-box-called-normal that gives me an opportunity for my own expansion. I sit with his openness, and my heart is full remembering the smiles and memories we brought to those who, in their diversity, teach us what is normal and natural inside all of our needs, wants, and desires.

I recently was contacted by Charlotte, an incredible woman from the UK who uses a wheelchair. She wrote this essay: "Being Held and Bodily Pride. What Touch Deprivation Does to the Self Esteem of Disabled People." The Knude Society

https://www.theknudesociety.com/the-society/being-held-and-bodily-pride-what-touch-deprivation-does-to-the-self-esteem-of-disabled-people

Conclusion

As you can see, the anomalies of diversity surround us in nature, in the animal kingdom, and in humanity. Not only in the physical realm but in our Plain Damn You. Creativity and the unique presence we each bring to this spinning ball we share, hurling us through space in a vast unknown infinity of diversity.

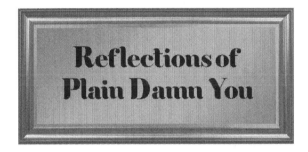

Reflections of Plain Damn You

1) What do you consider normal? Are there guidelines that you follow?

2) Do you think your nurturing outweighs the biology you were born with? Or vice versa?

3) Diversity in nature surrounds us. Does that give permission for diversity in ourselves and others?

4) Could fear and self-denial lead to a deep need for both neck-up and neck-down therapeutic intervention? If so, what might be a good next step?

Thoughts & Quotes

"Males do not represent two discrete populations; heterosexual and homosexual. The world is not to be divided into sheep and goats, and not all things are black nor all things white. It is a fundamental of taxonomy that nature rarely deals with discrete categories. Only the human mind invents categories and tries to force facts into separated pigeon-holes. The living world is a continuum in each and every one of its aspects. The sooner we learn this concerning human sexual behavior, the sooner we shall reach a sound understanding of the realities of sex." ~ Alfred Kinsey, *Sexual Behavior in the Human Male* 1948

"We are all different, which is great because we are all unique. Without diversity, life would be very boring." ~ Catherine Pulsife

The greater the diversity, the greater the perfection. ~

Thomas Berry

~*~

What divides us pales in comparison to what unites us. ~ Edward Kennedy

~*~

Diversity is the mix. Inclusion is making the mix work. ~ Andres Tapia

~*~

"The history of medicine proves that in so far as man seeks to know himself and face his whole nature, he has become free from bewildered fear, despondent shame, or arrant hypocrisy. As long as sex is dealt with in the current confusion of ignorance and sophistication, denial and indulgence, suppression and stimulation, punishment and exploitation, secrecy and display, it will be associated with a duplicity and indecency that lead neither to intellectual honesty nor human dignity." ~ "Sexual Behavior in the Human Male." Kinsey 1948

~*~

"What holds most people back isn't the quality of their ideas, but their lack of faith in themselves." - Russell Simmons

~*~

"Your life does not get better by chance. It gets better by change." - Jim Rohn

~*~

"The impression that infra-human mammals more or less confine themselves to heterosexual activities is a distortion of the fact which appears to have originated in a man-made philosophy, rather than in specific observations of mammalian behavior. Biologists and psychologists who have accepted the doctrine that the only natural function of sex is reproduction, have simply ignored the existence of sexual activity which is not reproductive. They have assumed that heterosexual responses are a part of an animal's innate, "instinctive" equipment, and that all other types of sexual activity represent "perversions" of the "normal instincts." Such interpretations are, however, mystical. They do not originate in our knowledge of the physiology of sexual response (Chapter 15) and can be maintained only if one assumes that sexual function is in some fashion divorced from the physiologic processes which control other functions of the animal body." ~ *Sexual Behavior in the Human Female*. Kinsey 1953

Conclusion The "Normal" Box Called Love

If you look up "love" in a dictionary, you will find an average of thirty-six definitions, approximately twelve columns on how we use the concept of love. Some are nouns, some verbs, both transitive and intransitive verbs. Love, apparently, plays an intricate role in our human experience. However, we put it in the confines of the "box" and relegate supposedly "normal" love mostly to couples (all flavors), family, our pets, the new hairstyle or football stadium seats. And, evidently, whatever our friends are sharing on social media.

I recently lost a relative, my cousin, who was my "out of the box" love connection from our childhood to adulthood. Everyone who knew us experienced the deep sharing and, dare I say, love we had for one another that was neither romantic nor familial, though he was like a brother to me.

We shared a declaration of love that understood each other with a look, a word of support or, more deeply, in silence. The bond that is shared through unconditional love, being there in times of struggle, depending on one another even when separated by distance. Those kinds of things we can count on that are missing in other relations. Those other relations may appear connected, but they are missing the bottom line, which is authentic love. And… found in the most unexpected places or "boxes."

My deepest desire was to see my life's mission manifest through completing this book and getting it out to the world. A fear accompanied that deep desire and had me spend four years mostly avoiding the work of writing this book. Then, ultimately, I sank my heart and soul into the project.

This journey revealed to me the understanding that humanity, in all its differences, diversities, and destructive behaviors, are all pieces of the jigsaw puzzle called life. You will find in these pages the opportunity to accept, surrender, and embrace that we are all on our own journey. Normal vs Natural, you decide. Are you here to leave your fingerprint? Your gifts? Your Plain Damn You?

In conforming to the "normal box," we sacrifice our opportunities to "know thyself" and be remembered for the unique human beings we truly are, leaving behind the memories that only You with You could imprint on the hearts and minds of those who are blessed to know us.

Thank you, Jay, for the memories and the love we shared that, I am grateful to say, was beyond normal.

Afterword

Google says: "An afterword is a literary device that is often found at the end of a piece of literature. It generally covers the story of how the book came into being."

Google says: The definition of a ghostwriter is someone who is a professional writer who helps the client write their book in exchange for money. Ghostwriters rarely take credit for their work.

Thus, here is the "afterword" and, I just could not let this book be published with me taking all the credit for the blood, sweat, and tears that it took for both me and my ghostwriter to make it a reality.

I came to know Nikki Leigh due to a colleague going through this birthing a book process with Nikki as her guide. When I decided to take this project on, I knew she was the guide I needed to literally hold my hand and pull me down this road. (A lot of the time kicking and screaming!)

Nikki and I have had a very sisterly connection as you can see in the photos. I became very close and bonded to her "kids" Muze (may he rest in peace) and Chloe, who warms my chair before I arrive in the morning with Chai Tea Lattes for Mom and me.

All kidding aside. Nikki is truly the main reason this accomplishment happened. She has authored (30+) of her own and ghost authored (25+) books.

> "Nikki Leigh is an award-winning author, a Certified Love and Relationship Coach, and a Certified Master Sexpert. She is also the host and producer of *Ready for Love Radio*, a weekly radio show, streamed to 196 countries on New Visions Radio since September 2013. (www.lovecoachjourney.com)."

I had to share how close we have become these last four years and that our relationship does not end here. Nikki will be involved with our IMBT family in various projects we are creating. Thank you, Nikki, from not only me but everyone who benefits from this book.

We had some rough brainstorming sessions…

Muze made appearances while we were working.

Chloe is warming Aunt Susan's chair.

We did it!

Appendix A – The Expanded Triadic Model

Before we explain the Expanded Triadic Model, it is important for you to understand the original Triadic Model that was developed by Bill Masters & Virginia Johnson. I have mentioned them a number of times throughout the book because the work they did is very integral to my work and to everyone who works in our field. Through my work, learning from them, and further study, I expanded the Triadic Model. That is the story I share with you here.

Masters & Johnson's Triadic Model

In 1957 Sex Researchers Masters & Johnson (M&J) began to collect groundbreaking data on sexual response. They used that data to create treatment plans for clients. The plans were based on talk and touch therapy. The clients would first speak with one of the therapists trained by M&J and then be given somatic homework. Think of talking as giving a client the map, and touch practices that allow the path to taking a walk. While this was great for couples, it left out singles who experienced their own sexual blocks. In 1969 M&J responded to the need of single males by introducing trained sex surrogates to their practice. So, there was the client with a sexual concern, a sex therapist, and a trained surrogate (substitute) partner. This trifecta was the first Triadic Model. I worked with M&J in the mid-1980s and also studied with them as my professors at the Institute for Advanced Studies of Human Sexuality in the mid-1990's. During this education, I saw the progress and understood the value of this unique therapy process of the triad model: including, Therapist, Surrogate, Client.

(https://en.wikipedia.org/wiki/Masters_and_Johnson)

(https://www.youtube.com/watch?v=xX-eSKXoqho)

Integrated Mind-Body Therapies Expands This Model

Masters and Johnson brought surrogate partners into the work to form the triadic model and this was a wonderful new dimension. Over time, and as my knowledge and skills have increased, I have adapted and expanded this triadic model. At Integrated Mind-Body Therapies, we incorporate surrogate partners into our work, and we also use a variety of other modalities. The modalities that are chosen for each client, depend on their individual background and their particular needs.

Talk Professionals and Touch Professional Collaborate at IMBT

At Integrated Mind-Body Therapy (IMBT) the Talk Pros (Therapists) and the Touch Pros (hands on) collaborate and work together for the well-being and healing of our clients. We will go into more detail about the variety of touch pros shortly.

These have been our biggest priorities when considering client care -

- How can **talk pros** and **touch pros** work more closely together to support their clients?

- What is the **Expanded Triadic Model**, and how can it benefit you in our practice?

- What is the **Expanded Triadic Model**, and how can it benefit you in our practice?

What is a Talk Professional

Talk Professionals – Those who support clients and/or patients primarily through discussion and conversation; minimal body-based interactions.

Some Examples of Talk Professional

- Mental Health Providers
- Sex Coaches
- Life Coaches
- Counselors
- Marriage and Family Counselors
- Sexuality Practitioners
- Educators
- Mindfulness Trainers

What is a Touch Professional

Touch Professionals – Those who support clients and/or patients primarily through touch and somatic (meaning body-based) interactions. Talk occurs, but it is not the primary focus.

Examples of Touch Professional

- Somatic Sexuality Educators

- Bodyworkers

- Surrogate Partners

- Health Workers

- Massage Therapists

- Sacred Intimates

- Professional Cuddlers

- Yoga Therapists

- Tantra Practitioners

Challenges for These Communities

- Practitioners are separated

- Skill sets are specialized to practices

- Knowledge across mind and body spectrum isn't always shared

- Clients/Patients have to "work across silos"

- Focus is rarely on integration of approaches

- Work can be lonely

Goal: Bring practitioners together and this is where Integrated Mind-Body Therapies excels.

- Offers an open, inclusive, integrated model

- Model encourages practitioner collaboration

- Enhancement to, not substitute for, existing practices

- Fosters community among practitioners

- Encourages knowledge sharing and skill development

Current Day Acceptance of Neck Up and Neck Down Therapeutic Modalities

Courageous historical sexologists created the cornerstone of what we know today as modern sex therapy. In this model many more professions can come to the table to provide wrap-around comprehensive therapeutic value to their clients to heal mentally, physically, emotionally, and dare I say spiritually.

"It is about time that resistance to the humanistic sexual healing approaches is addressed……It seems likely that resistance to the use of bodywork or group work or political action on the part of sexologists arose from the desire to adhere to the most respectable approaches to establish the legitimacy of the (sex field) profession. This in turn may arise out of embarrassment about sex itself, especially the respectability of sexual pleasure rather than sexual function as a focus of their work. But, it is no longer acceptable for professionals in the field of sex education, research, and therapy to fear being tainted by the subject matter."

"Sex Therapy As a Humanistic Enterprise." Published in Sexual and Relationship Therapy in 2006, Dr. Lenore Tiefer,

Everyone brings an important piece to a client's healing. This model continues to recognize the value and necessity of the role of the therapist, talk pro, and neck-up providers. In the past 20/30 years, several modalities focusing only on touch have gained mainstream acceptance. Body Electric, Sexological Bodywork, Tantra, Sacred Intimacy are well known not only in the states but around the world. While these practices and teachings have claimed a place on the stage of therapeutic practices, I still hold and maintain the need for the presence, supervision, and most importantly, that the primary decision-maker is someone with knowledge and tools from a "Neck Up" therapy background and viewpoint.

Appendix B – Ancient Seneca Wisdom About Touch

Melinda Joy and I met at a Children's Wellness Festival outside Philadelphia in 1985. She was my first body-mind massage teacher and through her studies with Grandmother Twylah, she introduced her students to various ancient healing tools for alignment of body, mind, and spirit wellness.

Melinda is teaching via zoom gatherings pertaining to Native American and cosmic events and through her books. Melinda's commitment to choosing to live a life of deep Joy is her core teaching which it would benefit the world to embrace.

Melinda shared this with me. It is taken from information Grandmother Twylah taught about touch from the Sacred Wisdom from the Ancient Seneca People. This was originally published in 1984.

Clan Destiny – Sensing

By Grandmother Twylah Hurd Nitsch

(Published year 1984)

Touch:

- to touch is to honor a sacred relationship

- The 'way of touching' evokes the virtues of all creations

- The initial Touch reveals potentials

- The 'gentle touch' perpetuates usefulness

What does Touch mean to Human People? Touching has a wide range of meanings - material and spiritual. Webster defines Touch materially as bodily contact with an object or a person; Striking with force; To stain, corrode, or decompose; Physical change; To retouch such as painting.

Spiritually, Touch soars into a wide dimension in which little is truly defined or realized. It is this idea we intend to pursue. The spiritual awareness of the Senecas and other natural Native People of this hemisphere.

To Touch is to Honor

- Everything on Earth touches.
- Touch pursues the purpose of every existence.
- The act of Touching can be described as stable, unchanged, constant.
- The result of Touch is unlimited.
- Therefore, Touch belongs to the sacred realm of our Creator and deserves this honor through self-understanding and Life's relationships.
- Touching supplies the direction toward evaluation of relationships
- We must emphasize the statement that

"Touch honors a sacred relationship."

"Touch emits a power of energy."

"Touch influences our senses."

- It is only through Touch that our senses respond.

- We are not always in direct control of our Touching.

- Every moment of our existence is spent in Touching, in one way or another.

- It is the 'lack of control' that creates our Life

experiences.

- "Touch exerts forces of multiple energies."

- We have a choice in the 'way' we touch:

- Positive = Peace or Negative = Fear

- These forces express their magnetic properties.

- The 'way' we touch evokes our virtues.

- Grappling, clutching, clawing, leaning, pulling, lifting are only a few examples of   strength and force that are experienced as a result of Touching.

- The initial Touch reveals our Life experiences.

Nature and Touch

- We look to Nature for our guidelines and examples.

- Nature expresses only POSITIVE direction.

- Her direction is toward perpetuation;

- Positive moves forward and upward -

- Negative   pulls   backward   to cause   a   vacillating

action between positive and negative.

- Nature's attitude of Touching teaches Peace.

- Negative powers create learning   experiences, thus are necessary for growth

Touch at Conception

- We must learn to enjoy the attitude of Peaceful Touch to secure a sense of touch.

- We 'Touch Earth' at conception and are 'Touched' by our Creator at Death.

- 'Touch' is the only element that creates the channel through which 'Feeling' may pass.

- There is no sensation expressed without the presence of 'Touch'

- We have limited awareness of 'Universal Touch' + Spirits + Thoughts + Feelings etc.

- Every entity in all creation is supported by the Element of Touch

- Without this Element of Touch, Peace would

disintegrate.

- Touch expresses quantities and qualities.

- **Quantities** reveal the molecular unity of every manifestation, be it material of spiritual - human or otherwise.

- **Quality** reveals its dimension of influence - good or bad.

- Personalities, appearances, lifestyles, and motivations are expressed by the way we Touch.

- We ask ourselves, "Why do I want to touch these things or these people?"

- To recognize these personal 'Touch Qualities' we must reach out to touch

- If we direct our way of Touch through the material into the spiritual, we can enrich our qualities of existence and express an aura of Peace.

- The way we Touch teaches us either experiences of happiness or strife

- Awareness of personal potential is realized when we reach out to Touch.

- Unhappiness, illness, accidents, poverty, bad habits and fear have been attributed to faulty Touch.

- This kind of Touch creates only pain - due to lack of balance.

- It is self-inflicted by our thoughts, attitudes, and limited understanding.

- We repeat that we are not always in control of our Touch. But, this is the reason we are here (living on Earth) To learn how to control our way of Touch.

- We must look around us and be truthful in asking, "Am I surrounding myself in an environment that stifles my growth, or one that enriches my awareness, my potential."

- Everything that is in existence is here because it has been initially Touched.

- This initial Touch creates its existence. But only if it continues to be useful can it express the Essence of the 'Gentle Touch'.

- The *gentle touch is that of the creator who gave us the power of touch with peace.'*

About Grandmother Twylah –

Grandmother Twylah Hurd Nitsch (1913-2007) an internationally known teacher of traditional wisdom of the ancient Seneca People taught through the Wolf Clan Teaching Lodge. The Senecas were the philosophers and teachers of the once powerful Iroquois Confederacy. Grandmother learned about the Wisdom, Prophecy and Philosophy of the Senecas first-hand from her grandfather, Moses Shongo, last of the great Seneca Medicine Men. Grandmother taught ways to observe the natural world with inner vision. - "It is our purpose in life to develop the inner self." Her mantra for sustainable living was "I am Grateful" and "All is One—One is All."

Poem *by Grandmother Twylah Hurd Nitsch*

We need to quiet down

Become one with the surroundings,

And be one with our fellow beings.

One of the first pathways to this goal

Is to feel comfortable by personally centering-in

With the powers of Earth-Harmony.

It is a natural path of human potential

That might be aimed toward Self-discovery and

development of the whole person,

Mentally, physically, emotionally, and spiritually.

For ten years Melinda Joy, studied with the Medicine Wheel of Peace/Cycles of Truth and ancient indigenous practices at the Cattaraugus Reservation near Buffalo, New York, with Grandmother Twylah. In July of 1992, Grandmother invited Melinda Joy to be a Keeper of the Medicine Wheel of Peace/ Cycles of Truth from the sacred teachings of the ancient Seneca People.

About Melinda Joy Miller –

Author, Speaker, Wellness Consultant, Student & Teacher of the Earth, Master Light Practitioner. She founded Shambhalla Institute in 1991 for the study and application of how the environment directly impacts one's quality of life. From 40 years involvement with healing arts, space clearing, permaculture, and spiritual retreats, Melinda Joy teaches Feng Shui, Shamanic Gardening, Medicine Wheel of Peace/Cycles of Truth, Light Practitioner Training.

Contact:

Melinda Joy Miller – Shambhalla Institute

https://shambhallainstitute.com

melindajoy.miller123@gmail.com

352-638-2617

Books by Melinda Joy Miller

Shine the Light: *A Personal Journey with Cancer & the Light*

Shamanic Gardener:Timeless Techniques for the Modern Sustainable Garden

Appendix C – Benefits of Journaling

Client Z came to us, in 2010, at fifty years of age and still a virgin. Z was living at home with his mom and dad.

Concerns he reported included discomfort in social situations, poor body image, and "fears around being naked with a woman." He also said, "The wall I keep up to be private even to be able to socialize with people has to be lowered and lowered even more with clothes off and lowered even more to have an erection." We discussed the skills he needed: the ability to speak up when he was embarrassed, dating skills, and tools to cope with anxiety, shame, and guilt.

We began with Z, as with most clients, to introduce the touch techniques of sensate focus. Z responded well to the tools and techniques of getting into his own body, releasing shame as he was able to share himself verbally and physically with the bodywork practitioner. The anxiety would still be present when the assignment was using his voice, speaking up, saying what he liked and what he didn't like, and facing fears of not crossing boundaries. "I know I am still self-spectatoring, evaluating myself because this is all new to me."

After several sessions his bodywork practitioner reported: "Z had gained very good communication skills and a lower anxiety level. He also 'allowed' feelings of warmth, compassion and connection."

Z gained tools from his work with us and progressed to doing well meeting girls, dating, getting past his view of himself as undesirable, and managing anxiety and shyness. He joined a fifty-plus dating site. Z has a love of dancing and has joined a meet-up group that dances several times a week. He is stretching himself and still wants to learn more about social cues going both ways: from him to her and her to him.

I continue to meet with Z a few times a year. Several years ago, he moved into his own apartment. He had a two-year relationship that was very emotionally, mentally, and physically rewarding. Z is now back into the dating scene and embraces his journaling therapy, as a journey to that place we call You with You.

Thank you, Z, for sharing these pages and a picture of your notebooks as you dance your way to You with Others.

Z shares his thoughts on keeping a journal: "I struggled a bit on writing this. I thought I would have more to write on the subject but in the end, the four points below are what I came up with."

Some Benefits of Journaling

1. Session Prep

Journaling helps record significant events that happen between therapy sessions. Prior to each session, it's helpful to review journal entries made since the last session and prepare a list of topics to discuss with your therapist. This ensures events don't get missed or forgotten, and any new concerns that arise are addressed in the session. Together, this helps keep the process moving forward.

2. Homework

The journal is the place to record important points made by your therapist during each session. You and your therapist will often decide on what you'll be working on between sessions. Record those tasks in the journal. This ensures you can refer to them over the coming days. You can also record the results of that work, so you can report back to your therapist with any progress or setbacks you may have had while working on these tasks. This is also convenient when you want to repeat these exercises again later.

3. Seeing Your Progress

Rereading old journal entries can really help you see the progress you're making. After enough time goes by, the older entries will seem to be from a different person—they are from the person you used to be. The person you are now has learned and grown and is not the same person who made the old entries.

4. Recall and Refresh

Since the therapy process can take time, it's easy to forget things you learned earlier in the process. Referring to detailed notes makes it easier to recall and refresh your memory on things you learned in the past. So, it's also important to date entries in the journal so they can be found later. You can highlight significant events or breakthroughs with sticky notes so they can be found quickly and reread. It's like having your therapist beside you, repeating what you've learned in previous sessions. For example, if you feel anxiety rising before an upcoming event, rereading the relevant journal entries will remind you of the anxiety management techniques you've learned during the therapy process, and this helps circumvent the old, automatic anxiety reaction that might otherwise occur.

** You may want to leave several blank pages at the front of the journal so that you can note special details and page numbers. This can include special events and accomplishments or special instructions or exercises from your therapists. That will make it easy to refer to them in the future. You can also add these notes in the back if you prefer or just use sticky notes to mark the pages. Whichever way works best for you.

Appendix D – Recommended Resources

Dr Kaye's Recommended Books

Sinless Sex: A Challenge to Religions **by William Stayton**

Hardcover – https://www.amazon.com/Sinless-Sex-Challenge-William-Stayton/dp/1643885618

Kindle - https://www.amazon.com/Sinless-Sex-Challenge-William-Stayton-ebook/dp/B08PNCKLB8

Ethical Use of Touch in Psychotherapy **by Mic Hunter & Jim Struve**

Hardcover – www.amazon.com/Ethical-Use-Touch-Psychotherapy-dp-0761903607

Paperback – https://www.amazon.com/Ethical-Touch-Psychotherapy-Political-Culture-dp-0761903615/dp/0761903615

Kindle - https://www.amazon.com/Ethical-Touch-Psychotherapy-Political-Culture-ebook-dp-B00ZA7RCSG/dp/B00ZA7RCSG

The Surgeon General's Call to Action To Promote Sexual Health and Responsible Sexual Behaviors 2001

This publication is available to download as a PDF file on the Health and Human Services website at https://www.ncbi.nlm.nih.gov/books/NBK44216/pdf/Bookshelf_NBK44216.pdf or you can read it online at https://www.ncbi.nlm.nih.gov/books/NBK44216/

Sex is the Least Of It by Tova Feder

Paperback – https://www.amazon.com/Sex-Least-Surrogate-Partners-Intimacy/dp/0692288597

Kindle - https://www.amazon.com/Sex-Least-Surrogate-Partners-Intimacy-ebook/dp/B00LH5WJLK

The Art of Receiving and Giving: The Wheel of Consent by Betty Martin

Paperback – https://www.amazon.com/Art-Receiving-Giving-Wheel-Consent/dp/1643883089/

Kindle - https://www.amazon.com/Art-Receiving-Giving-Wheel-Consent-ebook/dp/B08YMZK3T9

The Body Keeps the Score by Bessel Van Der Kolk, M.D.

Hardcover – https://www.amazon.com/Body-Keeps-Score-Healing-Trauma/dp/0670785938

Paperback – https://www.amazon.com/Body-Keeps-Score-Healing-Trauma/dp/0143127748/

Kindle - https://www.amazon.com/Body-Keeps-Score-Healing-Trauma-ebook/dp/B00G3L1C2K

Somebody Hold Me by Epiphany Jordan

Paperback – https://www.amazon.com/Somebody-Hold-Me-Persons-Nurturing/dp/1732879206/

Kindle - https://www.amazon.com/Somebody-Hold-Me-Persons-Nurturing-ebook/dp/B07MM6FFBD

8 Erotic Nights: Passionate Encounters that Inspire Great Sex for a Lifetime by Charla Hathaway

Hardcover – https://www.amazon.com/Erotic-Nights-Passionate-Encounters-Lifetime/dp/1592333109

Kindle - https://www.amazon.com/Erotic-Nights-Passionate-Encounters-Lifetime-ebook/dp/B004GHNP32

The Five Love Languages by Gary Chapman

Paperback – https://www.amazon.com/Love-Languages-Secret-that-Lasts/dp/080241270X/

Kindle - https://www.amazon.com/Love-Languages-Secret-that-Lasts-ebook/dp/B00OICLVBI

Touching: The Human Significance of the Skin by Ashley Montagu

Hardcover – https://www.amazon.com/Touching-human-significance-Ashley-Montagu/dp/0060155353

Paperback – https://www.amazon.com/Touching-Human-Significance-Ashley-Montagu/dp/0060960280

Caring, Feeling, Touching by Sidney Simon

Paperback – https://www.amazon.com/Caring-feeling-touching-Sidney-Simon/dp/0913592676

Touch in the Helping Professions: Research, Practice and Ethics by Martin Rovers, Judith Malette, and Manal Guirguis-Younger

Paperback – https://www.amazon.com/Touch-Helping-Professions-Research-Practice-dp-0776627554/dp/0776627554

e-Textbook - https://www.amazon.com/Touch-Helping-Professions-Research-Practice-ebook-dp-B097J5QZKR/dp/B097J5QZKR/

On a Clear Day: A Coloring Book for Healing Trauma by An iregina Chronicle

https://www.balboapress.com/en/bookstore/bookdetails/800426-on-a-clear-day

For the kid in you or kids you care about:

Bellybuttons are Navels by Dr. Mark Schoen

Hardcover – https://www.amazon.com/Bellybuttons-Are-Navels-Young-Readers/dp/0879755857

Paperback – https://www.amazon.com/Bellybuttons-Are-Navels-Mark-Schoen/dp/1419686534

Kindle - https://www.amazon.com/Bellybuttons-Are-Navels-Mark-Schoen-ebook/dp/B007O0P7OS

"Historic" Content

Massage Therapy Journal Newsletters

There are great articles in the pages of these newsletters. These can be found on the Google Books app and online at **www.books.google.com**. Search for individual topics or "Massage Therapy Journal".

The Power of Touch - It might be the most essential and least appreciated sense. Are you getting touched enough? -

by David Linden and Martha Thomas, AARP The Magazine, December 2015/January 2016

https://www.aarp.org/health/healthy-living/info-2015/power-of-touch.html

Recommended Viewing & Listen*ing* -

Dr Susan Kaye on YouTube –

https://www.youtube.com/channel/UChmhQ2c6bLHFJfwwzPlsVgg

Ready for Love Radio with Nikki Leigh

Thursday 9 pm ET US www,newvisionsradio.com

Archive - https://podcasts.bcast.fm/ready-for-love-with-nikki-leigh-love-coach

Ready for Love Radio Recommended Shows –

Surrogate Partner Training in Sex is the Least of It with Tova Feder

https://podcasts.bcast.fm/e/x8vm465n-sex-is-the-least-of-it-with-tova-feder-ph-d

A Cuddlist and Platonic Touch Therapist with Jasmine Siemon

https://podcasts.bcast.fm/e/rnkppm18-a-cuddlist-and-a-platonic-touch-therapist-with-jasmine-siemon

Surrogate Partner Therapy Training

https://podcasts.bcast.fm/e/1n2mr418

Sex Smart Films with Mark Schoen

https://podcasts.bcast.fm/e/5nz1k928

Flirting and Body Language with the Dignified Hedonist

https://podcasts.bcast.fm/e/v8w1k1y8

Recovering Touch with Dr Susan Kaye

https://podcasts.bcast.fm/e/xn1q4pjn

Code of Ethics for Practitioners with Paul Bagge

https://podcasts.bcast.fm/e/18pxp038

Sexual Energy and Surrogate Partners with Tova Feder and Paul Bagge

https://podcasts.bcast.fm/e/r876wj7n

Am I Normal If with Dr Susan Kaye

https://podcasts.bcast.fm/e/v85v53jn

Importance of Touch with Paul Bagge

https://podcasts.bcast.fm/e/r8k2p3pn

Let's Talk About Diversity with Dr Susan Kaye

https://podcasts.bcast.fm/e/v85v6wmn

Appendix E – World Association for Sexual Health Declaration of Sexual Rights

The WAS Declaration of Sexual Rights was reviewed in the year 2014 by a special working group and an expert consultation convened by the World Association for Sexual Health.

WAS Declaration of Sexual Rights 2014 English

(English version - https://worldsexualhealth.net/wp-content/uploads/2021/09/declaration_of_sexual_rights_sep03_2014_b.pdf)

Declaración de Derechos Sexuales 2014 Español

(Spanish version - https://worldsexualhealth.net/wp-content/uploads/2021/09/declaracion_derechos_sexuales_sep03_2014_b.pdf)

Text version - https://worldsexualhealth.net/wp-content/uploads/2013/08/Declaration-of-Sexual-Rights-2014-plain-text.pdf

Sexual Health and Sexual Rights are FUNDAMENTAL for Well-being

WAS 4O YEARS

WORLD ASSOCIATION FOR SEXUAL HEALTH

DECLARATION OF SEXUAL RIGHTS

In recognition that sexual rights are essential for the achievement of the highest attainable sexual health, the World Association for Sexual Health:

STATES that sexual rights are grounded in universal human rights that are already recognized in international and regional human rights documents, in national constitutions and laws, human rights standards and principles, and in scientific knowledge related to human sexuality and sexual health.

REAFFIRMS that sexuality is a central aspect of being human throughout life, encompasses sex, gender identities and roles, sexual orientation, eroticism, pleasure, intimacy, and reproduction.

Sexuality is experienced and expressed in thoughts, fantasies, desires, beliefs, attitudes, values, behaviours, practices, roles, and relationships. While sexuality can include all of these dimensions, not all of them are always experienced or expressed. Sexuality is influenced by the interaction of biological, psychological, social, economic, political, cultural, legal, historical, religious, and spiritual factors.

RECOGNIZES that sexuality is a source of pleasure and wellbeing and contributes to overall fulfillment and satisfaction.

REAFFIRMS that sexual health is a state of physical, emotional, mental and social wellbeing in relation to sexuality; it is not merely the absence of disease, dysfunction or infirmity. Sexual health requires a positive and respectful approach to sexuality and sexual relationships, as well as the possibility of having pleasurable and safe sexual experiences, free of coercion, discrimination and violence.

REAFFIRMS that sexual health cannot be defined, understood or made operational without a broad understanding of sexuality.

REAFFIRMS that for sexual health to be attained and maintained, the sexual rights of all persons must be respected, protected and fulfilled.

RECOGNIZES that sexual rights are based on the inherent freedom, dignity, and equality of all human beings and include a commitment to protection from harm.

STATES that equality and non-discrimination are foundational to all human rights protection and promotion and include the prohibition of any distinction, exclusion or restriction on the basis of race, ethnicity, colour, sex, language, religion, political or other opinion, national or social origin, property, birth or other status, including disability, age, nationality, marital and family status, sexual orientation and gender identity, health status, place of residence, economic and social situation.

RECOGNIZES that persons' sexual orientations, gender identities, gender expressions and bodily diversities require human rights protection.

RECOGNIZES that all types of violence, harassment, discrimination, exclusion, and stigmatization are violations of human rights, and impact the wellbeing of individuals, families and communities. AFFIRMS that the obligations to respect, protect and fulfill human rights apply to all sexual rights and freedoms.

AFFIRMS that sexual rights protect all people's rights to fulfill and express their sexuality and enjoy sexual health, with due regard for the rights of others.

Sexual rights are human rights pertaining to sexuality:

1. The right to equality and non-discrimination

Everyone is entitled to enjoy all sexual rights set forth in this Declaration without distinction of any kind such as race, ethnicity, color, sex, language, religion, political or other opinion, national or social origin, place of residence, property, birth, disability, age, nationality, marital and family status, sexual orientation, gender identity and expression, health status, economic and social situation and other status.

2. The right to life, liberty, and security of the person Everyone has the right to life, liberty, and security that cannot be arbitrarily threatened, limited, or taken away for reasons related to sexuality. These include: sexual orientation, consensual sexual behavior and practices, gender identity and expression, or because of accessing or providing services related to sexual and reproductive health.

3. The right to autonomy and bodily integrity Everyone has the right to control and decide freely on matters related to their sexuality and their body. This

includes the choice of sexual behaviors, practices, partners and relationships with due regard to the rights of others. Free and informed decision making requires free and informed consent prior to any sexually related testing, interventions, therapies, surgeries, or research.

4. The right to be free from torture and cruel, inhuman, or degrading treatment or punishment Everyone shall be free from torture and cruel, inhuman, or degrading treatment or punishment related to sexuality, including: harmful traditional practices; forced sterilization, contraception, or abortion; and other forms of torture, cruel, inhuman, or degrading treatment perpetrated for reasons related to someone's sex, gender, sexual orientation, gender identity and expression, and bodily diversity.

5. The right to be free from all forms of violence and coercion Everyone shall be free from sexuality related violence and coercion, including: rape, sexual abuse, sexual harassment, bullying, sexual

exploitation and slavery, trafficking for purposes of sexual exploitation, virginity testing, and violence committed because of real or perceived sexual practices, sexual orientation, gender identity and expression, and bodily diversity.

6. The right to privacy Everyone has the right to privacy related to sexuality, sexual life, and choices regarding their own body and consensual sexual relations and practices without arbitrary interference and intrusion. This includes the right to control the disclosure of sexuality-related personal information to others.

7. The right to the highest attainable standard of health, including sexual health; with the possibility of pleasurable, satisfying, and safe sexual experiences Everyone has the right to the highest attainable level of health and wellbeing in relation to sexuality, including the possibility of pleasurable, satisfying, and safe sexual experiences. This requires the availability, accessibility, acceptability of quality

health services and access to the conditions that influence and determine health including sexual health.

8. The right to enjoy the benefits of scientific progress and its application Everyone has the right to enjoy the benefits of scientific progress and its applications in relation to sexuality and sexual health.

9. The right to information Everyone shall have access to scientifically accurate and understandable information related to sexuality, sexual health, and sexual rights through diverse sources. Such information should not be arbitrarily censored, withheld, or intentionally misrepresented.

10. The right to education and the right to comprehensive sexuality education Everyone has the right to education and comprehensive sexuality education. Comprehensive sexuality education must be age appropriate, scientifically accurate, culturally competent, and grounded in human rights, gender

equality, and a positive approach to sexuality and pleasure.

11. The right to enter, form, and dissolve marriage and other similar types of relationships based on equality and full and free consent Everyone has the right to choose whether or not to marry and to enter freely and with full and free consent into marriage, partnership or other similar relationships. All persons are entitled to equal rights entering into, during, and at dissolution of marriage, partnership and other similar relationships, without discrimination and exclusion of any kind. This right includes equal entitlements to social welfare and other benefits regardless of the form of such relationships.

12. The right to decide whether to have children, the number and spacing of children, and to have the information and the means to do so Everyone has the right to decide whether to have children and the number and spacing of children. To exercise this right requires access to the conditions that influence and

determine health and wellbeing, including sexual and reproductive health services related to pregnancy, contraception, fertility, pregnancy termination, and adoption.

13. The right to the freedom of thought, opinion, and expression Everyone has the right to freedom of thought, opinion, and expression regarding sexuality and has the right to express their own sexuality through, for example, appearance, communication, and behavior, with due respect to the rights of others.

14. The right to freedom of association and peaceful assembly Everyone has the right to peacefully organize, associate, assemble, demonstrate, and advocate including about sexuality, sexual health, and sexual rights.

15. The right to participation in public and political life Everyone is entitled to an environment that enables active, free, and meaningful participation in and contribution to the civil, economic, social, cultural,

political, and other aspects of human life at local, national, regional, and international levels. In particular, all persons are entitled to participate in the development and implementation of policies that determine their welfare, including their sexuality and sexual health.

16. The right to access to justice, remedies, and redress Everyone has the right to access to justice, remedies, and redress for violations of their sexual rights. This requires effective, adequate, accessible, and appropriate educative, legislative, judicial, and other measures. Remedies include redress through restitution, compensation, rehabilitation, satisfaction, and guarantee of non-repetition.

*** The World Association for Sexual Health (WAS) is a multidisciplinary, world-wide group of scientific societies, NGOs and professionals in the field of human sexuality which promotes sexual health throughout the lifespan and through the world by developing, promoting and supporting sexology and sexual rights for all. The WAS accomplishes this by advocacy actions, networking, facilitating the exchange of information, ideas and experiences and advancing scientifically based sexuality research, sexuality education and clinical sexology, with a trans-disciplinary approach. The WAS Declaration of Sexual Rights was originally proclaimed at the 13th World Congress of Sexology in Valencia, Spain in 1997 and then, in 1999, a revision was approved in Hong Kong by the WAS General Assembly and then reaffirmed in the WAS Declaration: Sexual Health for the Millenium (2008). This revised declaration was approved by the WAS Advisory Council in March, 2014.

https://worldsexualhealth.net/wp-content/uploads/2013/08/Declaration-of-Sexual-Rights-2014-plain-text.pdf

Appendix F Dr. William Stayton's Panerotic Potential Model

William Stayton has suggested a model of sexual orientation that broadens the focus of the Kinsey Sexual Orientation Scale and Fred Klein's Sexual Orientation Grid, by acknowledging the possibility that individuals can find erotic nurturance and intimacy in almost anything in the universe. (Used with permission from William Stayton.)

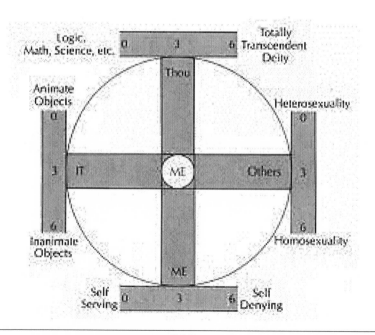

About Susan Kaye, PhD

Susan Kaye, Sexologist, Founder of Integrative Mind-Body Therapies, LLC, is a sexual wellbeing specialist with a Ph D in Human Sexuality, and 30 years of experience as a somatic practitioner. She has expertise as a tantra teacher, bodywork practitioner, Esalen massage therapist, and yoga instructor. She also has decades of working in the sexual health field as a Sexologist, Sex Coach and Sex Educator.

Why work with Susan? Longevity. She began her career working with cutting-edge Sexological Researchers Bill Masters and Virginia Johnson. She has been speaking and teaching their Body Mind Healing Process for the past 30 years. Their research on arousal and pleasure, and the activities they developed to increase those feelings, is what sex therapists around the world use to structure client care.

These combined years of bringing body and sex positive teachings to communities around the country has required multiple leaps of faith. There have been explanations at family dinners and hopping on many lily pads to become a trained bodywork therapist as well as a clinical counselor and coach. She believes in offering clients total mind body wellness by connecting them with talk therapists as well as somatic experts to help them embody the healing they are seeking.

Dr Susan Kaye Website - http://drsusankaye.com/

Integrative Mind-Body Therapies LLC - https://imbtinternational.com/

https://www.facebook.com/Dr.SusanKaye

About Nikki Leigh

Nikki Leigh is an award-winning author, a Certified Love and Relationship Coach and the host of Ready for Love Radio, the international radio show, streamed to 196 countries each week on New Visions Radio (www.newvisionsradio.com) and many shows are on the top podcast directories. The show has aired over 400 shows as over July 2022.

Nikki's experience as a love coach transcends the topical 'walls' of intimacy and dating as she tackles a wide variety of topics, including ones that can be very difficult to discuss personally or professionally. She shares these messages through her blog, her books, coaching, and her Love, Accept and Respect Yourself Program and her Ready for Love Radio show. Details can be found on www.lovecoachjourney.com.

Combine her work with her experience as a coach, an interviewer and radio host, and it has helped her develop a winning combination with her *Ready for Love* radio show. That has created a successful radio show that has endeared her to millions of loyal listeners around the world and enabled her to attract feature guests with many different expertise, including nationally and internationally known experts in their fields.

Ready for Love Radio –

https://podcasts.bcast.fm/ready-for-love-with-nikki-leigh-love-coach

Love Coach Journey - www.lovecoachjourney.com